A2 Music
Harmony Workbook

Hugh Benham

Edited by
Paul Terry

RHINEGOLD
EDUCATION

www.rhinegoldeducation.co.uk

Rhinegold Music Study Guides

GCSE, AS and A2 Music Study Guides (AQA, Edexcel and OCR)
GCSE, AS and A2 Music Listening Tests (AQA, Edexcel and OCR)
AS/A2 Music Technology Study Guide (Edexcel)
AS/A2 Music Technology Listening Tests (Edexcel)
Revision Guides for GCSE (AQA, Edexcel and OCR), AS and A2 Music (Edexcel)

Also available from Rhinegold Education

Key Stage 3 Listening Tests: Book 1 and Book 2
AS and A2 Music Harmony Workbooks
GCSE and AS Music Composition Workbooks
GCSE and AS Music Literacy Workbooks
Romanticism in Focus, Baroque Music in Focus, Film Music in Focus,
Modernism in Focus, Musicals in Focus
Music Technology from Scratch
Dictionary of Music in Sound

First published 2009 in Great Britain by
Rhinegold Education
14–15 Berners Street
London W1T 3LJ
www.rhinegoldeducation.co.uk

© 2009 Rhinegold Education
a division of Music Sales Limited

Rhinegold Education has used its best efforts in preparing this guide. It does not assume, and hereby
disclaims any liability to any party, for loss or damage caused by errors or omissions in the guide, whether such
errors or omissions result from negligence, accident or other cause.

If you are preparing for an exam in music you should always check carefully
the current requirements of the examination, since these may change from one year to the next.

A2 Music Harmony Workbook
Order No. RHG428
ISBN 978-1-906178-39-0

Exclusive Distributors:
Music Sales Ltd
Distribution Centre, Newmarket Road
Bury St Edmunds, Suffolk IP33 3YB, UK
Printed in the EU

Contents

About the author

Hugh Benham is a chair of examiners for GCE Music, an in-service trainer, church organist and writer. He has contributed to *Music Teacher* and *Classroom Music* magazines, and is the author of *Baroque Music in Focus* (Rhinegold, 2007). His other writing includes two books on English church music, including *John Taverner: his Life and Music* (Ashgate, 2003), articles on early music, and contributions to *The New Grove Dictionary of Music and Musicians* (2001) and *Die Musik in Geschichte und Gegenwart*. He edited Taverner's complete works for *Early English Church Music* (Stainer and Bell). Hugh was formerly head of music in a sixth-form college.

Acknowledgements

The author would like to thank Paul Terry for his many editorial suggestions, Bruce Cole for his advice on Chapter 4, and Dr Lucien Jenkins and Katherine Smith of Rhinegold Publishing for their help and encouragement in the preparation of this book.

Introduction

Using this book

This workbook gives detailed information on, and practice exercises in, some of the most widely offered harmony and counterpoint tasks for GCE A2 Music. You won't need to study all four chapters – your teacher will point to the right one(s) for the course you are taking.

You should have already worked through the *AS Music Harmony Workbook*, because it provides the basic knowledge and skills needed to tackle A2 work. Continue to use the AS workbook for revision and reference as you study the present volume.

The four chapters

In Chapter 1 we deal with harmonising chorales in the style of J. S. Bach, beginning with preparatory work and cadences. 'Bach chorales' are an option in the A2 Music specifications offered by Edexcel, OCR and AQA, and feature in many other music examinations at Level 3 and beyond.

The subject of Chapter 2 is late-Baroque two-part counterpoint. We begin by explaining figured bass, techniques of melodic decoration, dissonance, modulation and imitation. We then address in detail the technical study option for Edexcel A2 Music (adding a melody above a figured bass and adding a bass with figuring below a given melody for violin or flute). The chapter ends with study of two-part counterpoint for keyboard, an option for OCR A2 Music.

In Chapter 3 we discover how to complete simple Classical string-quartet textures in which the first-violin part alone is given, an option for both OCR and AQA A2 Music. An introduction to the basics of writing for string quartet (ranges, clefs, score layout, and so on) leads on to detailed advice about choosing appropriate chords for the style, and adding idiomatic inner parts.

Chapter 4 is designed principally for those who intend to offer Popular Song as their submission for Edexcel's A2 Music technical study. Chord symbols are explained, and there is plenty of advice on how to add a melody above a bass with chord symbols, and how to add a bass and chord symbols below a given melody, in ballad-song style. Students offering the Popular Song option for OCR's A2 Music will also find some of this chapter useful.

Activities

All chapters include activities to help you learn and remember what you have read. These are not just exercises to write out. They are intended above all to help you think in terms of real sounds. So it is important to sing, hum, whistle or play everything. Don't worry about the sound you make so long as the notes are correct. Use whatever assistance you can find – ask a friend or teacher to play your work, notate it on screen and play it back through the speakers on your computer, or play four-part harmony as a piano duet – the options are endless.

Consult if in doubt!

Many technical terms will be explained as we go along, but if anything is not clear, don't gloss over it – ask your teacher for help.

1   Chorales

A chorale is a type of hymn that was traditionally sung in the Lutheran (Protestant) churches of Germany. The harmonisations of these tunes by J. S. Bach (1685–1750) have long been regarded as excellent models of four-part vocal writing.

Bach's settings can be found in a book called *Bach, 371 Harmonized Chorales and 69 Chorale Melodies with Figured Bass* edited by Albert Riemenschneider (published by Schirmer). This widely-available collection is commonly known as *Riemenschneider*. In this chapter the letter *R* plus a number refers to a chorale in *Riemenschneider*.

1.1   Chorales in exams

Harmonising a chorale in the style of J. S. Bach is an option in many music examinations at A level and beyond. Normally the full harmony of the opening bars is given, to provide a starting point and a guide to the style required. It is useful in the early stages to concentrate on cadences and their approaches, but first we must cover some important preliminaries.

1.2   Writing for four-part choir

When writing chorale harmonisations it is best to keep within the vocal ranges shown in Example 1.2. The soprano range is included for reference, although this part is normally given in exam questions.

Bass parts occasionally go a note or two lower than shown here – for example, at the end of a phrase in order to reach a low dominant or tonic in a perfect cadence.

In the rest of this chapter, we often refer to the soprano, alto, tenor and bass parts as S, A, T and B for short.

Chorales are normally written in short score – that is, with S and A on a treble stave, and T and B on a bass stave. The stems for S and T always go up, while those for A and B always go down, as in Example 1.4.1 on the next page.

1.3.   The chorale style

Here are some important points about the style of Bach's chorales, each of which we will explore in more detail later:

✦ Each phrase ends with a cadence, shown by a pause sign (⌢) on the last chord of the cadence.

✦ The majority of cadences are perfect, with both $V^{(7)}$ and I in root position. Most of the rest are imperfect cadences, often with the first chord in first inversion.

✦ Chords usually change on every beat until a cadence. One or both chords of the cadence itself may last for more than one beat, but this is not always the case.

✦ Bach makes much use of primary triads in root position and first inversion, but other chords also appear, including II^7b (often used before a perfect cadence).

- Some phrases are likely to modulate to closely-related keys.

- In many chorales, non-chord notes keep up an almost continuous flow of quaver movement until each cadence. However, the final chord of a cadence is not usually decorated – there is normally a clean break before the next phrase begins.

- Bach's chorales are basically homophonic, with the lower parts supporting the chorale melody, but each of the lower parts, particularly the bass, has some rhythmic and melodic interest and character.

A few of Bach's chorale settings have a special chromatic intensity, often because of words that refer to suffering or death. However, these are exceptional and unlikely to appear in exams. Indeed, exam exercises do not as a rule provide any words, but are concerned just with the musical content and style of Bach's more typical settings.

1.4 Spacing of chords

The first kind of spacing shown in Example 1.4.1 *below* sounds well when sung by a four-part choir, and is very common in Bach's work. It has a larger interval between T and B than between any other two neighbouring parts, which helps to make the bass part (with its vital harmonic function) stand out clearly.

The second type of spacing in Example 1.4.1 has small intervals at the top and bottom of the texture, and a large gap in the middle. This rarely sounds good for voices, and you would be wise to avoid it.

Ex. 1.4.1

Try to avoid having more than an octave between any two of the three upper parts, but remember that a bigger gap between T and B is fine. Here is an important tip that will help you capture Bach's style in your own work:

- **Keep the tenor part high.**

Bach's tenor parts are frequently on leger lines well above middle C. One of the most common faults in chorale tests is writing tenor parts that are far too low.

It may help to think of spacing in terms of keyboard playing. Many four-part vocal chords are easier to play with three notes in the right hand and one note in the left than with two notes in each hand. For instance, the last four chords of Example 1.4.2 (i) could be played as shown in Example 1.4.2 (ii).

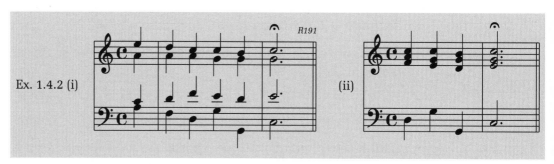

Ex. 1.4.2 (i)   R191   (ii)

However, remember that chorales were not written as keyboard pieces, nor were they conceived as just successions of block chords. Each of their four vocal parts needs to have some rhythmic and melodic interest for the singers.

Here is a short passage designed for playing in the '3 + 1' manner shown in the previous example. Notice how little the top three parts move, each relying a good deal on stepwise movement, as many simple chorale textures do.

R303 (adapted)

1.5 Doubling

A note is **doubled** if it appears more than once in a chord (either at the same pitch or in different octaves).

Since you are writing for four voices, but using mainly triads (three-note chords), most chords in a chorale are likely to include a doubled note. Even four-note chords, such as dominant 7ths, may sometimes need to have a note doubled (and therefore some other note omitted) in order to achieve a good sense of line in each vocal part.

For a broad outline of how doubling works in triads and 7th chords, revise section **2.16** of the *AS Music Harmony Workbook* (page 31). Here now is some more detail.

$\frac{5}{3}$ **chords**
+ **Normally double the root**, so that the chord consists of two roots, a 3rd and a 5th. You can instead have three roots and a 3rd, which means having no 5th in the chord, although Bach himself rarely does this.

+ **Never omit the 3rd** – the result sounds bare and, without a 3rd, the chord isn't clearly major or minor.

$\frac{6}{3}$ **chords**
+ **Double any pitch that is note 1, 4 or 5 of the key you are in**. For example, if you use chord iib in the key of G major, double the note C, which is note 4 in the scale of G major. This method is easy to remember if you think of the notes to double (1, 4 or 5) as the 'primary notes' of the scale (just as I, IV and V are primary chords). It doesn't matter whether the doubled note is the root, 3rd or 5th of the chord.

+ Alternatively, **double the root of the triad** (except in *viib*, because doubling the root in that chord would mean doubling the leading note, which you should always avoid).

+ **Other notes can be doubled** instead, if this seems more sensible in context, but always remember never to double the leading note in any chord.

All chords
+ **Don't double any of the tendency notes** (7ths, chromatic notes or dissonant notes as well as the leading note). This is because any such doubling will result in consecutives when both tendency notes resolve in similar fashion. If you need to double a note in a 7th chord it is best to double the root and omit the 5th.

There are a couple of more advanced points about doubling later in this chapter, in Sections **1.8** and **1.11**.

(a) The following $\frac{5}{3}$ chords all lack an alto part, a tenor part or both. Add appropriate notes so that each has two roots, a 3rd and a 5th. Be sure to follow the advice on chord spacing given in Section **1.4** (page 6).

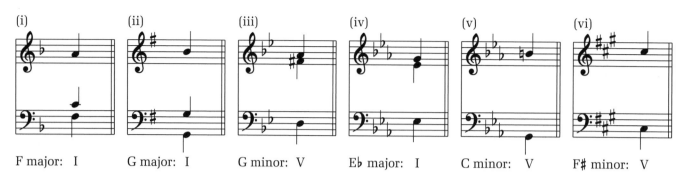

(b) The following $\frac{6}{3}$ chords lack both middle parts. Add appropriate notes to complete each one, explaining which note you've doubled.

Write more than one completion if you can find two or more possible answers.

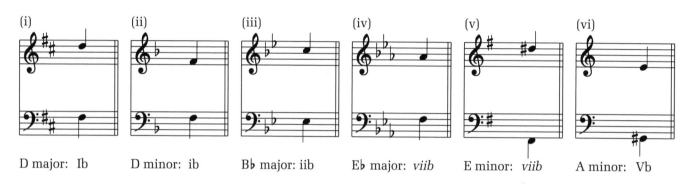

1.6 Writing cadences

Because cadences are so important in tonal music, it is best to begin our work on completing chorales by harmonising the cadences. In Bach's chorales, most cadences are either:

✦ **Perfect** ($V^{(7)}$–I), or

✦ **Imperfect** (ending on V).

There are not many plagal or interrupted cadences in Bach's chorale harmonisations. In fact, an interrupted cadence is never *essential* since a perfect cadence can always be used instead.

The type of cadence you write depends on the notes in the given melody. It can be helpful to associate particular pairs of scale degree numbers in a given melody with particular types of cadence. For example, you can harmonise a melodic phrase that ends with notes 2 and 1 with a perfect cadence: chord V goes with note 2 and chord I goes with note 1.

However, remember that chorale harmonisation is not 'composing by numbers'. Always try to hear and think about what you write.

We explored writing cadences in the *AS Music Harmony Workbook* (pages 35–39 and 90–92), so let's summarise the steps involved:

1   Identify the key at the end of the phrase.

2   Identify the scale numbers of the final two notes (for example, 7–8).

3   Decide which type of cadence will best fit these notes, and write out the notes of the chords you will need.

4   Work out what the bass notes are, and write them in.

5   Add the alto and tenor parts.

6   Check everything carefully, as explained on the next page.

1.7 Perfect cadences

Example 1.7.1 shows a phrase from a chorale. Working through steps 1–3 *above* will tell you why this phrase must finish with a **perfect cadence**.

1   The phrase ends in D major.

2   The two last notes of the phrase (E–D) are scale degrees 2–1.

3   The notes 2–1 will fit with a perfect cadence. Write down the notes needed for a perfect cadence in D major, perhaps on a mini-stave, as shown *left*.

Moving on to steps 4 and 5:

4   As most perfect cadences in chorales have both chords in root position, the bass part here can be A for chord V and D for chord I. A falling 5th from A to D would work, but a rising 4th from the lower A to D is better since it provides desirable contrary motion between the outer parts, as shown in Example 1.7.2 *below*.

5   Adding the inner parts – it is often best to do this one chord at a time.

After step 4, chord V has an A and an E, but it lacks a 3rd (C♯). This has to go in the alto part since C♯ a 3rd above the bass note would be awkwardly low for tenors, while middle C♯ (an octave higher) would leave no room for an alto note. With all three notes of the triad now accounted for, the tenor must double a note, preferably the root (A).

After step 4, chord I has a doubled root (D), so the inner parts need to supply the 3rd (F♯) and preferably also the 5th (A).

Can you spot the 'error' in this example? The leading note (C♯) in the alto doesn't rise to the tonic (D) in the way expected of a tendency note. In fact, this is not an error, but an important feature of Bach's chorale harmonisations:

✦ **If the leading note occurs in the alto or tenor at a perfect cadence, it often falls *directly* to the 5th of the tonic chord.**

Bach does this in order to achieve a complete and full-sounding tonic chord at the cadence, rather than the thinner sound of one without a 5th. You can see the difference by comparing versions (i) and (ii) in Example 1.7.3 *below*. Also, Bach occasionally allows a leading note in the tenor to leap upwards to the 3rd of the tonic chord at a cadence, again to achieve a complete tonic chord, as shown in (iv) *below*.

Such treatments of the leading note at cadences are a distinctive feature of Bach's chorales and you should try to use them whenever appropriate. But remember that the leading note should fall *directly* to the 5th of the tonic chord Bach never uses a passing note between the two, as shown in Example 1.7.3 (iii). Be very careful about this, as spoiling a falling leading note by inserting a passing note to fill the gap is a common mistake in exams.

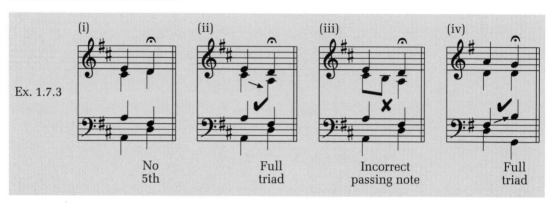

Ex. 1.7.3

(i) No 5th   (ii) Full triad   (iii) Incorrect passing note   (iv) Full triad

Before we move on to the final step in cadence writing, there is one improvement we can make to the cadence shown in (ii) *above*. In Section **1.3** we noted that

Ex. 1.7.4

Correct passing note

✦ In many chorales, non-chord notes keep up an almost continuous flow of quaver movement until each cadence.

While a passing note in the alto would be incorrect, there is an opportunity for an excellent passing note in the *tenor*, between A and F♯. This involves a G, giving a passing 7th above chord V that neatly resolves to F♯. This is very much in keeping with Bach's methods and helps provide the really stylish result shown *left*.

All that now remains is to carry out the last of our six steps:

6 Check everything carefully on paper and by playing your work. Make sure that you have:

    ✦ Used the right notes for the chords concerned

    ✦ Doubled (or omitted) notes correctly

    ✦ Spaced the notes so that there is no large gap between S and A, or A and T

    ✦ Used conjunct movement or only small leaps in the upper three parts

    ✦ Ensured that any tendency note in the first chord moves to the correct note in the second chord (remembering Bach's special treatment of the leading note when it occurs in an inner part of chord V at a perfect cadence)

    ✦ Avoided consecutive 5ths or consecutive octaves between any of the parts.

If anything is wrong, correct it and then perform this check again.

The fall from note 2 to note 1 in the soprano that we harmonised in this section is the most common melodic pattern in perfect cadences. Example 1.7.5 shows four more 2–1 perfect cadences from Bach's chorales. The last of these ends with a tierce de Picardie (explained on page 49 of the *AS Music Harmony Workbook*). Each of the arrows shows a leading note that does *not* rise to the tonic.

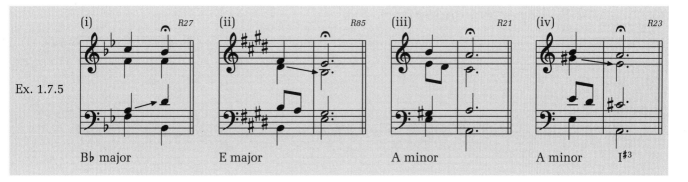

Ex. 1.7.5

Bb major — E major — A minor — A minor $I^{\sharp 3}$

Perfect cadences will also harmonise the melodic patterns 7–8, 2–3 and 5–3, as shown in Example 1.7.6. Cadence (iii) in this example shows the pattern 2–3 harmonised with an inverted perfect cadence (Vb–I). An inverted cadence is one in which one (or both) of the chords is inverted. Inverted perfect cadences are much rarer than root position ones, and are never used at the end of a chorale.

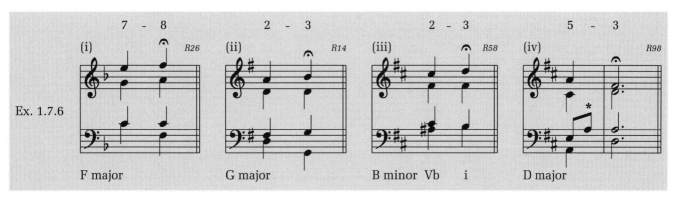

Ex. 1.7.6

F major — G major — B minor Vb i — D major

Activity 1.7

(a) Which cadences in Example 1.7.5 at the top of this page include a dominant 7th as a passing note?

(b) Which of the following describes the note marked * in cadence (iv) of Example 1.7.6 *above*?   auxiliary note   harmony note   passing note   appoggiatura

(c) Write a perfect cadence at the end of each of the following four chorale phrases. Follow the six steps outlined earlier, be sure to play your work, and remember to check it using the checklist printed in Step 6 *opposite*.

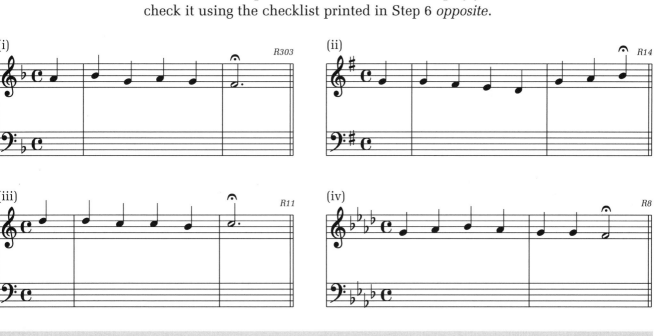

1.8 Imperfect cadences

In Bach's chorale harmonisations, roughly one in four cadences is imperfect. The following phrase requires an **imperfect cadence**. If you follow steps 1–3 you'll see why.

Ex. 1.8.1

1   The key is A major.

2   The phrase ends with C♯–B, which are notes 3–2 in the scale of A major.

3   The cadence cannot be perfect, because B does not occur in the tonic chord. However, there is a B in chord V (E, G♯, B) and a C♯ in chord I (A, C♯, E) so we can harmonise C♯–B with I–V, making an **imperfect cadence**.

Notes 3–2 at the end of a phrase almost always suggest an imperfect cadence.

Ex. 1.8.2

Look at the example *above* as we continue with steps 4–6.

4   The bass must have A for chord I and E for chord V. It would be possible to fall from an upper A to the E, but rising a 5th from the lower A to the E provides desirable contrary motion between the outer parts.

5   Both chords are in root position, so double the root in each, and keep the inner parts as still as possible. The big gap (a compound 5th) between bass and tenor is perfectly acceptable.

6   As always, carefully check your work.

Doubling the major 3rd

Ex. 1.8.3

Our imperfect cadence, with its two root-position chords, works satisfactorily, but Bach himself used Ib rather than plain I for the first chord (shown *left*). In fact, he often preferred to start imperfect cadences with a first-inversion chord – something to bear in mind when trying to recreate his style.

The part-writing in Example 1.8.3 may strike you as wrong, because the first chord has a **doubled major 3rd** (C♯ in each of the outer parts). However, Bach uses this pattern so often that it is well worth learning as an exception to the usual principle of doubling a primary note or the root (see Section **1.5**) in a $\frac{6}{3}$ chord. When Bach uses this kind of doubled major 3rd, note that (as here):

✦   Outer parts move in contrary motion while inner parts move as little as possible

✦   The bass includes a passing note between Ib and V.

The next example shows some more imperfect cadences in which notes 3–2 are harmonised with the progression I–V or Ib–V. Note that Bach did *not* use Ic–V as an imperfect cadence in his chorales.

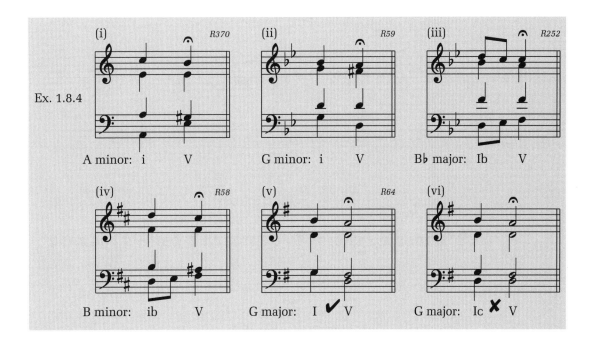

Ex. 1.8.4

(i) R370 — A minor: i — V
(ii) R59 — G minor: i — V
(iii) R252 — B♭ major: Ib — V
(iv) R58 — B minor: ib — V
(v) R64 — G major: I ✔ V
(vi) G major: Ic ✘ V

Where imperfect cadences have something other than 3–2 movement in the melody, a chord from the subdominant group will often fit – generally IV$^{(7)}$b or II$^{(7)}$b, as shown in Example 1.8.5. Notice how, in the first two of these cadences, Bach uses quaver decoration to maintain movement through the first (but not the second) chord of the cadence:

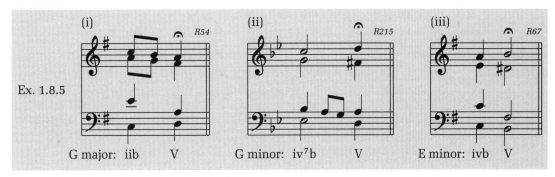

Ex. 1.8.5

(i) R54 — G major: iib — V
(ii) R215 — G minor: iv^{7}b — V
(iii) R67 — E minor: ivb — V

Example (iii) *above* is a **phrygian cadence** (ivb–V *in a minor key*) – a type of imperfect cadence often used to harmonise notes 4–5 in minor-key cadences.

Activity 1.8

(a) Look again at cadence (i) in Example 1.8.5 *above* and then explain why Bach doubled the 5th of chord V instead of the root in this cadence.

(b) Why should notes 1–2 never be harmonised with chords IV–V? If this seems puzzling, try writing this progression in the key of C major, and note the problem it raises.

(c) Write an imperfect cadence at the end of each of the following phrases.

(i) R64

(ii) R37

Turn the page for question (d).

(d) Write an imperfect cadence at the end of this phrase.

R78

1.9 Choosing chords to approach a perfect cadence

The *AS Music Harmony Workbook* has general information about approach chords on pages 35–37 and 93–95. What follows here is specific to chorales.

First, a general point. It's best to change harmony on each crotchet beat (except on a long pause chord, which should have only one chord). In particular, don't repeat the same chord from a weak to a strong beat in your cadential progression – Bach normally does this only at the *start* of an anacrusic phrase, such as the opening of *R6* in Activity 1.16.2 on page 32). In common time (**C** or $\frac{4}{4}$), the weak beats are 2 and 4.

Here's how to choose the chord immediately before a perfect cadence for some common melodic patterns. In all cases, the first and second notes are crotchets. The third note (the last of the phrase) may be a crotchet or longer.

Chord I as an approach

The first chord of a perfect cadence is, of course, chord V. It is often approached directly from Ib or Ic – or even from plain chord I. An approach from a chord in the subdominant group is another possibility, especially ii⁷b, as explained *opposite*.

Example 1.9.1 at the top of the next page illustrates settings of some of the most common melodic patterns as well as some features of Bach chorales that should by now be becoming familiar:

✦ The first three cadences each include a passing 7th in the tenor, and most include at least one passing note.

✦ Cadences (i), (iv) and (vii) have doubled major 3rds in chord Ib (as explained on page 12) with the characteristic passing note in the bass between Ib and V.

✦ Cadences (ii), (iii) and (x) have chord Ic as the approach chord. Remember that the 4th above the bass in Ic (the E in cadence (ii), for example) is considered dissonant with the bass. Bach normally requires this 4th to be **prepared**.

✦ Cadences (ii), (iii) and (viii) include falling leading notes in an inner part, all of which leap directly to the 5th of chord I *without* an intervening passing note.

✦ Cadence (iii) includes a lower auxiliary in the bass (C) and finishes with a tierce de Picardie (as do perfect cadences at the *end* of most minor-key chorales).

In cadence (xi) Bach harmonises the melodic pattern 6–7–8 with the progression IV–V–I. This is potentially risky because the similar motion between S and B in chords IV–V can make consecutive 5ths or octaves in the middle parts difficult to avoid. In cadence (xii) Bach harmonises the same melodic pattern with IV–*viib*–I. Substituting *viib* for V allows contrary motion between the outer parts and so greatly reduces the risk of consecutives.

Chord ii⁷b as an approach

Sometimes the penultimate note of a phrase is a minim – usually as the middle note of the melodic pattern 3–2–1. This minim is often harmonised with *two* separate

chords. The chord schemes for this pattern, shown in Example 1.9.2 *below*, also work for the similar four-crotchet pattern 3–2–2–1: just imagine the minim on pitch 2 split into two crotchets. For ease of reference, we will use the abbreviation 3–2–2–1 both when we have a four-crotchet pattern, and when pitch 2 last for two beats.

Ex. 1.9.2

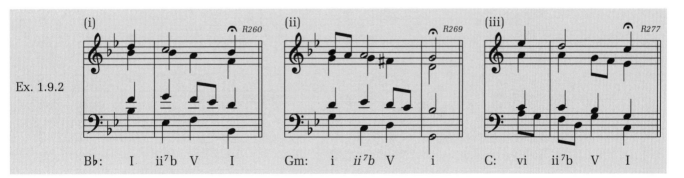

All these progressions use **II⁷b as the cadence approach chord**. And in every case Bach follows what was his standard procedure: the 7th of chord ii⁷b is treated as a **suspension** that resolves to the leading note – which in turn falls to the 5th of the tonic chord. Trace this pattern in the alto part of cadences (i) and (ii) *above*, and in the tenor part of cadence (iii).

For more about the circle of 5ths, see pages 40–41 of the *AS Music Harmony Workbook.*

This pattern also works well for melodies ending 8–8–7–8, in which the second 8 can be treated as a suspension in the soprano part. In the next example, as in (iii) *above*, Bach approaches *ii⁷b* from chord VI, so that each chord in the progression is a 5th lower than the previous one, resulting in part of a **circle of 5ths**.

Ex. 1.9.3

Bm: VI   ii⁷b   V   i

Suspensions are also common where Bach decides to harmonise a minim on pitch 2 with just a single chord V. Two full beats of plain chord V would be very dull, so he uses a 4–3 suspension to keep up the musical interest. In Example 1.9.4 this occurs in the alto part in (i) and the tenor part in (ii). Compare the treatment of these dissonances with the 7ths in Example 1.9.2 on the previous page. In all five cases, the suspended note is the tonic, which resolves to the leading note before falling to the 5th of the tonic chord. (You may find it useful to remember that the dissonant 4th of Ic is also the tonic, and it too resolves to the leading note in chord V.)

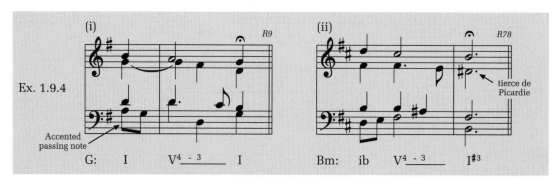

Ex. 1.9.4

(i)   R9
Accented passing note

G: I   V⁴ ₋ ³   I

(ii)   R78
                                              tierce de Picardie

Bm: ib   V⁴ ₋ ³   I#3

Here are two more examples of ii⁷b used as a cadence approach chord, this time in the melodic pattern 4–3–2–2–1. In Example 1.9.5 (i), you could regard the second quaver beat as consisting of three simultaneous passing notes, or as creating chord Ic in passing. In Example 1.9.5 (ii), the Ic seems more like a chord in its own right. However, because all of its notes either move by step or stay put, it could again be viewed as a $\frac{6}{4}$ made up of passing notes.

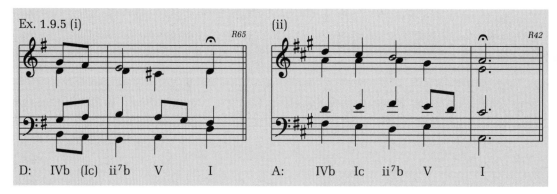

Ex. 1.9.5 (i)   R65

D: IVb   (Ic)   ii⁷b   V   I

(ii)   R42

A: IVb   Ic   ii⁷b   V   I

This progression, and the cadential Ic–V–I, are the *only* uses of $\frac{6}{4}$ chords normally found in chorales. Even these are used quite sparingly.

V⁷ of V as an approach

Occasionally Bach gives a perfect cadence a specially intense chromatic 'twist' by sharpening the 3rd (which is in the bass) of chord ii⁷b, which turns the chord into a secondary dominant, V⁷ of V. Remember that the 5th of this chord will also have to be raised if in a minor key. If you are unsure about secondary-dominant chords, revise pages 47–48 of the *AS Music Harmony Workbook*.

Cadence (i) in the next example shows V⁷ of V used to approach a perfect cadence in a major key – notice that this progression also includes a passing $\frac{6}{4}$. V⁷ of V is more often used as an approach chord to perfect cadences in *minor keys* – an example is shown in cadence (ii) *below*. If you decide to use this device, do so sparingly and remember to add the necessary accidentals (including any needed to cancel chromatic notes).

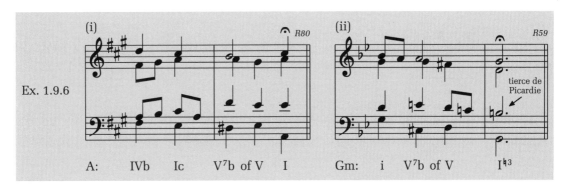

Ex. 1.9.6

A: IVb   Ic   V⁷b of V   I   Gm: i   V⁷b of V   I⁴³

Activity 1.9

Add bass parts and Roman numerals (but not inner parts) to harmonise the following melodic patterns, which should each end with a perfect cadence.

Gm: C: F: Dm:

1.10 Choosing chords to approach an imperfect cadence

The most basic type of imperfect cadence is I–V, and Bach generally approaches this from chord V$^{(7)}$b or its close relative, chord *viib*. Example 1.10.1 *below* demonstrates some of the possibilities.

The first three progressions in this example are all from the same chorale and show how Bach sought to achieve variety, even when faced with similar cadences in the same key. All three patterns work equally well in major keys. Progression (iv) uses *vii⁷* as an approach chord which, in a minor key as here, is a diminished 7th chord.

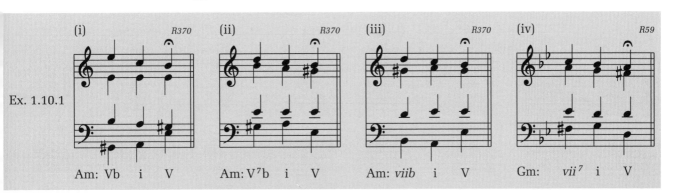

Ex. 1.10.1

Am: Vb   i   V   Am: V⁷b   i   V   Am: *viib*   i   V   Gm: *vii⁷*   i   V

Other approach chords include I, IV or VI – the choice depends on creating contrast with the first chord of the cadence as well as harmonising the given melody:

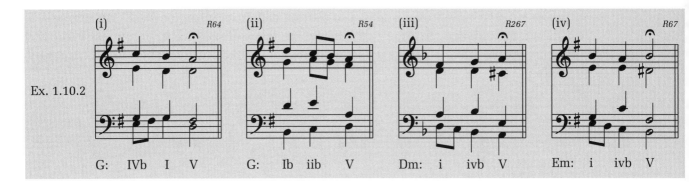

Ex. 1.10.2

(i) R64 — G: IVb I V
(ii) R54 — G: Ib iib V
(iii) R267 — Dm: i ivb V
(iv) R67 — Em: i ivb V

Sometimes the first note of an imperfect cadence is a minim, as shown in Example 1.10.3 (i) *below*, or there are two crotchets of the same pitch before the last chord of the cadence, as shown in (ii).

In such cases it is often not possible to use different chords for the two crotchet beats, as we did in the perfect cadences on the previous page. However, as you can see in Example 1.10.3 *below*, Bach doesn't merely write a minim in all parts for the first chord, or repeat it exactly on the second crotchet beat. Instead he maintains a sense of movement through the use of passing notes and/or additional harmony notes. Notice the way in which the downward octave leap in the bass of cadence (i) gives impetus to the second beat of the bar without altering the harmony.

In cadence (ii) Bach provides variety by moving from chord i to chord ib below the repeated C in the melody. This progression, from root position through the first inversion of the same chord with the bass rising through quaver passing notes, is often used by Bach – and not only in cadences.

The first of these progressions uses V^{7}b as an approach chord. The second has ivb.

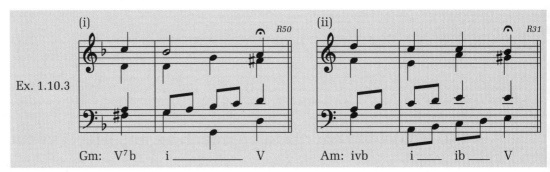

Ex. 1.10.3

(i) R50 — Gm: V^{7}b i _____ V
(ii) R31 — Am: ivb i ___ ib ___ V

Activity 1.10

(a) What type of melodic decoration is used in (i) the alto part and (ii) the tenor part of Example 1.10.2 (iii) at the top of this page?

(b) What name is given to the particular type of imperfect cadence shown in Example 1.10.2 (iv) at the top of this page?

(c) Add bass parts and chord symbols (but not inner parts) to harmonise the following melodic patterns, which should each end with an imperfect cadence.

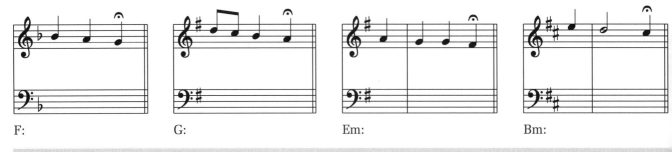

F: G: Em: Bm:

1.11 Part-writing in chorales

This section summarises a number of general points about part-writing that we discussed in Chapter 4 of the *AS Music Harmony Workbook*, and introduces some new matters that are specific to part-writing in chorales.

Crossing parts Avoid crossing parts by, for instance, letting the alto fall below the tenor, or the tenor fall below the bass. Although Bach occasionally does this, you will be well advised to avoid any part-crossing, unless you are absolutely certain that it is in Bach's style and makes the music better than it otherwise would be.

Overlaps An overlap occurs if two neighbouring parts, such as tenor and bass, move so that the lower part in the second chord is higher than the upper part in the first chord, or vice versa, as shown in Example 1.11.1 (i) and (ii) *below*. Bach occasionally overlaps parts where he considers that this will add special interest to the part-writing. However, it is generally best for us to avoid overlaps (perhaps by choosing a different note to double) since they can easily add confusion instead of interest.

There are, though, a few circumstances in which overlaps are fine:

+ The first usually involves T and B, and is shown in progression (iii) *below*. Here two notes a 3rd apart move to a unison, the bass leaping up a 4th. Often this type of overlap involves movement from a dominant and a leading note in chord V to unison tonic notes in chord I, as it does in this example.

+ The second is simply the reverse of the first (unison T and B moving down to a 3rd by step and by a 4th respectively), usually with chords I–V.

+ The third happens between the end of one phrase and the start of the next, as shown in (iv) *below*. Such overlapping can be effective when, as here, the new phrase doesn't start with a change of chord, and so needs a different layout of notes in order to sound distinct.

Ex. 1.11.1

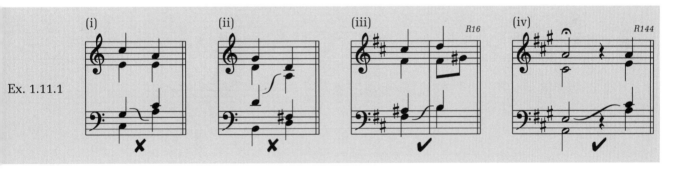

Doubling Revise the advice on doubling in the *AS Music Harmony Workbook*, page 31, and in particular remember that:

+ Tendency notes must not be doubled – you must therefore not double the leading note or any dissonant note (for example, the 4th above the bass in a 4–3 suspension, or the 7th of a seventh chord).

+ It's rarely necessary to double the 5th in root-position triads.

+ Bach sometimes doubles the 3rd in first-inversion triads, and occasionally even in root-position triads. When he does this, he often has contrary motion to and from the doubled 3rd (as in the third chord in Example 1.12.4 on page 23).

+ Diminished triads (chord *vii*, plus chord *ii* in minor keys) are often used in first inversion with the bass note (the 3rd of the chord) doubled.

+ In chord Ic, the 5th should be doubled.

Dissonances

✦ All suspensions, along with the 7th in chord ii^7(b) should always be prepared as well as resolved. The 7th in chord V^7 can be treated a little more freely, but if it is not prepared then it should be approached by step, as shown in the first cadence of Example 1.11.2 *below*.

✦ The effect of a suspension is spoiled if the note of resolution occurs at the same time in another part:

  ✦ For instance, if an F is suspended over a chord of C major, the resolution (E) should appear only in the part that sounded the suspension and not in any other part.

  ✦ The one exception is a 9–8 suspension, in which the note of resolution will already be present in the bass below the suspended note.

✦ Bach regarded a 4th above the bass as a dissonance, and therefore his standard practice is to prepare it in the preceding chord. (Occasionally he did approach the 4th by step from above, but as a rule there's no need for you to do this.)

✦ When using the cadential $^6_4$ (in Ic–V–I), treat the 4th above the bass in chord Ic as a dissonance. Prepare it if you can, as shown at * in Example 1.11.2 (ii) *below*, otherwise approach it *by step from above*, as shown at * in cadence (iii). In both cases, the dissonant 4th (circled in these examples) must move down by step to resolve.

  ✦ Don't forget to double the 5th of chord Ic (in other words, the dominant note), not the root or the 3rd.

  ✦ Let the 3rd in Ic (the 6th above the bass) fall by step to the 5th of chord V. This creates parallel 3rds or 6ths with the part in which the 4th above the bass resolves, as shown by the arrows in cadences (ii) and (iii):

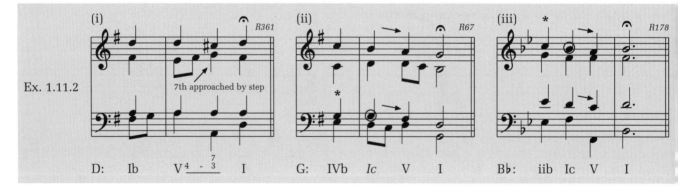

Ex. 1.11.2

Consecutives

✦ Parallel perfect 5ths, octaves or unisons between any pair of parts must be avoided.

✦ A perfect 5th followed by a diminished 5th (or vice versa) must not be used between the bass and an upper part, and is best avoided between any pair of parts.

✦ If you have too much similar motion between soprano and bass, there is a danger not only of consecutive 5ths and octaves, but also of **exposed 5ths** or **exposed octaves**. These can only occur between the outer parts, and only within a phrase (not between the end of one phrase and the start of the next). They happen where the soprano *leaps* and the bass moves in the same direction (by step or leap) so that the two parts arrive on a perfect 5th or an octave, as shown in parts (i) and (ii) of Example 1.11.3 at the top of the next page. They sound poor because the perfect intervals concerned are too prominent – too 'exposed'.

✦ In the outer parts it is also preferable to avoid consecutive 5ths or octaves even when produced by contrary motion. These **5ths and octaves by contrary motion** are shown in parts (iii) and (iv) of Example 1.11.3:

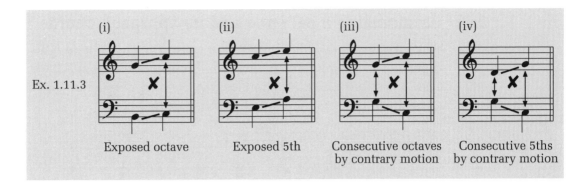

Ex. 1.11.3

(i) Exposed octave
(ii) Exposed 5th
(iii) Consecutive octaves by contrary motion
(iv) Consecutive 5ths by contrary motion

Consecutive 5ths and octaves, as you've probably gathered, are particularly bad *between the outer parts*. Because of this, never add A and T until you are sure there are no consecutive 5ths or octaves (including any by contrary motion) or exposed 5ths or octaves between S and B.

Then complete A and T, aiming for as much conjunct movement as possible, and finally carry out checks on all six pairs of parts:

◆ S and A   S and T   S and B
  A and T   A and B   T and B.

Sometimes it isn't easy to remove consecutives. If they exist between S and B before passing notes have been added, the choice of chords is faulty, so choose one or more different chords. If consecutives arise between other pairs of parts, the doubling in one or more chords may be unsuitable.

Too much similar motion between soprano and bass sometimes makes it difficult to avoid consecutives between other parts. They are far less likely to arise if **the bass moves in contrary motion to the soprano** as much as possible.

Activity 1.11

In the following two passages, someone who has not read section 1.11 carefully has made a number of mistakes, including awkward part-crossing, incorrect doubling, poor chord-spacing, overlapping and consecutives.

Find and label each mistake – the first one has been done for you.

Octaves by contrary motion

1.12 Harmonising a cadence and its approach chords

The following example contains a phrase from a chorale. We have to supply the cadence and its approach chord in full four-part harmony. Notice that, as usual with exam questions based on chorales, the opening chords are given in full. These help to establish the key and may offer other helpful clues.

Ex. 1.12.1

Here's how to complete the exercise.

1   Identify the key

The key is F major.

2   Decide on the type of cadence, and then choose the approach chord

Identify the scale degree numbers of the last two notes of the phrase (G–F): they are 2–1 in the scale of F major. A perfect cadence will fit, with bass notes C and F. Write these notes in, and mark the two chords V and I. *Which* F goes in the bass – low F just below the stave or F an octave higher? The lower F has more weight and finality, and this choice also reflects Bach's preference for a falling 5th in the bass (rather than a rising 4th) at a perfect cadence.

As you know, when scale degree 2 occurs either twice before the last note of a phrase (as two crotchets) or once as a minim, ii⁷b makes an excellent approach to a perfect cadence. The bass note of this chord (B♭) will fit neatly between the given A and the C of chord V, and – most importantly – the 7th of ii⁷b (which is F) can be prepared by the alto F in the last of the given chords. We now have the following outline:

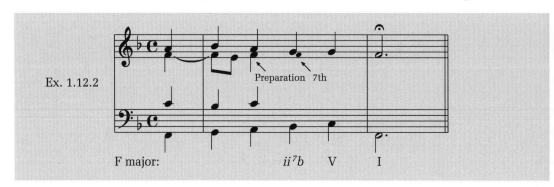

Ex. 1.12.2

3   Check the outer parts for consecutives

Before adding inner parts, check that there are no consecutives between S and B. Don't forget that these can occur between the last given notes of the phrase and your added notes, as well as within your own working. As ever, the risk of consecutives is reduced if you write your bass mainly in contrary motion to the melody.

4   Add the alto and tenor parts

Follow the usual methods for spacing and doubling. Keep the tenor high and juggle the notes until you get as much conjunct movement as possible.

Check that the inner parts of your first chord do not produce consecutives with the preceding given chord and make sure that if you use chords such as Ic or ii⁷b, the discord is prepared, sounded and resolved in the same part (as shown by the letters P, S and R in the example below):

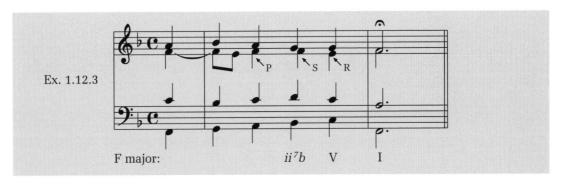

Ex. 1.12.3

F major: ii⁷b   V   I

This is a good harmonisation, but it doesn't entirely capture Bach's style. For instance, it would be more convincing if the alto fell to C at the end to complete the final tonic chord and provide Bach's characteristic falling leading note at a perfect cadence. But the main missing ingredient is the rhythmic flow produced by melodic decoration.

5 Add melodic decoration

This is best done after checking that the inner parts are free of consecutives. Remember that it is never necessary to force decoration onto *every* beat, and that the pause chord of the cadence should not normally be decorated at all.

It is usually best to keep to quavers for decoration. Bach never uses triplets – when he needs a three-note pattern he generally uses the rhythm ♩♫, although even this is rare.

The commonest type of melodic decoration is the passing note, linking two pitches a 3rd apart. We can add a B♭ quaver passing note in the tenor at the penultimate chord. This is sufficient melodic decoration, given the simple rhythmic style of the phrase as a whole. Remember to add melodic decoration with discretion, not just for the sake of padding.

6 Final check

Here now is our final version, including the falling leading note in the alto part at the perfect cadence, and the passing note in the tenor:

Ex. 1.12.4

F major: ii⁷b   V   I

Check that all your chords are correct, any accidentals needed have been included (particularly important in minor keys) and that, after adding decoration, there are still no consecutives in any of the six pairs of parts.

Notice that the third of the given chords in this example is a major triad with a doubled major 3rd (the note A in the outer parts). As usual when employing this doubling, Bach ensures that the major 3rd is approached and quitted by step, with contrary motion between the parts concerned.

(i) Complete the harmonisation of the following phrase, to end with an imperfect cadence in F major.

(ii) Complete the following passage by adding cadences and approach chords at the ends of the second, third and fourth phrases. This exercise is quite plain in style, so there will be little or no opportunity to add melodic decoration.

The third phrase is clearly in the dominant – you will find that the second phrase is much easier to harmonise if you treat it as also being in the dominant key.

Be particularly careful to avoid consecutive 5ths and/or octaves in bar 6 *above*. The progression IV–V–I (in the dominant key) will fit the given melody but root-position triads a step apart (IV–V) can easily result in all parts moving in similar motion and thus lead to consecutives. Alternatives include:

✦ The progression ii–V–I in the dominant (you may need to double the 3rd of chord ii, which will be the note A)

✦ The progression IV–*viib*–I in the dominant. Chord *viib* is a close relative of V and Bach sometimes uses it in place of the dominant chord (although not at the end of a chorale, where the full authority of a V–I cadence is required). An example of *viib* used in this way can be seen in cadence (xii) on page 15.

1.13 Spotting a modulation

The third phrase in Activity 1.12 (ii) clearly modulates to E major because of D♯–E in the given melody and the need for a perfect cadence underneath it. However, it is not so obvious that the second phrase should modulate. The change of key is implied rather than explicitly indicated, because there is no tell-tale D♯ in the given melody. Nevertheless, E major is a more likely key for this phrase because:

✦ The concluding F♯–E in the melody points to E major (remember that many chorale phrases end with scale degrees 2–1)

✦ If it had stayed in A major, the G♯ in the melody would have been the leading note and would therefore be expected to rise to the tonic. The fact that it doesn't do so suggests that the music may no longer be in A major.

Look out for such clues, as most chorales are likely to include at least one phrase that modulates. In short chorales, such phrases usually end with a **perfect cadence in the new key**. The dominant or relative major are the most likely keys for a modulation, but any related key is possible. Look at the following melody:

Ex. 1.13   Freylinghausen's *Gesangbuch*, 1704

This melody may appear to be in D major throughout, but there are two clues as to why it should not be harmonised entirely in that key:

1   There is again a leading-note in the melody (marked *) which does not rise to the tonic. This is a pretty sure sign of modulation and, since the phrase ends with 3–2–2–1 in the scale of A major, the dominant is the most likely key for the end of this second phrase.

2   The third phrase ends with the melodic pattern 3–4 in D major (bar 6), and there is no cadence that would support this combination of pitches. We therefore need to think what else might be possible. V–I in G major (the subdominant key) will work, as will V–I in E minor, the relative minor of the subdominant. The latter might be preferable as it gives a valuable touch of minor-key contrast in an otherwise completely major-key piece.

It's not unusual for there to be a choice of key for any given melodic phrase. For instance, the first phrase *above* could end with V–I in B minor. The choice depends on context. Here, the first cadence would really be too early for a modulation – so it would be preferable to harmonise it as a perfect cadence in the tonic.

Acticity 1.13

(a) Suggest keys and cadences for the phrases in the following chorale melody. The first answer is given.

Anon. (1653), modified by Crüger

G minor: perfect

Turn the page for more questions.

(b) Complete the cadences, including suitable approach chords, in each of the following chorales. Think carefully about the key for each cadence. The first phrase of chorale (iii), which we previously encountered on page 101 of the *AS Music Harmony Workbook*, could end with a phrygian cadence.

(i)

Melody: Johann Crüger, 1647 (adapted)

(ii)

Melody: Halle, 1704

(iii)

Melody: *Nürnbergisches Gesangbuch*, 1676

1.14 Anacrusic openings

When shortly we come to work on complete chorales, we shall need to harmonise beginnings of phrases as well as endings. Those many chorale phrases that begin with an **anacrusis** (up-beat) need special consideration.

Sometimes an anacrusic start will suggest a progression based on chords V and I, as at (i) in Example 1.14 *below*. However, in many cases Bach repeats an opening tonic chord on the first beat of the next bar. This is an important exception to the convention that the same chord should not normally be repeated from a weak to a strong beat. However, note that Bach often includes an upward leap of an octave in the bass, as in cadence (ii) *below* in order to give the down-beat chord greater rhythmic impetus.

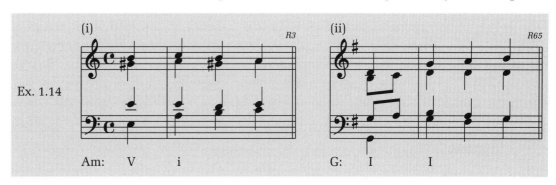

Ex. 1.14

1.15 Harmonising a complete chorale melody

Chorale exercises for A2 Music, and for some other exams, require the harmonisation of a complete melody. While this involves more work than just adding a cadential progression, the basic method is the same. Indeed, it is a good idea to start with the cadences and their approach chords, and then tackle the start of each phrase.

In this section we shall work through the steps needed to harmonise the chorale melody in Example 1.15.1 *below*. As usual in harmonisation exercises, the first few beats have already been completed. These are useful in indicating the style expected, particularly with regard to the amount of melodic decoration.

Ex. 1.15.1

1 Identify the keys throughout the exercise

In most cases you should expect the last phrase to be in the same key as the start of the chorale, and for at least one of the phrases before the end to modulate and cadence in a related key.

In this chorale melody, there are no accidentals to suggest a specific modulation, but we should still expect a modulation to be implied somewhere. Three of the four phrases end with a fall of a major 2nd. Those that finish G–F clearly represent scale degrees 2–1 in F major and demand perfect cadences in that key. But what about the phrase that ends D–C? Name a suitable key, related to F major, that could support a perfect cadence on these two notes.

2 Identify each cadence, including approach chords, then write in the bass notes

This is similar to work we have done previously, so do this for yourself now, and then compare your answers to the suggestions below.

Phrase 1 The melody ends with 2–2–1 in F major, inviting a perfect cadence in the tonic. We should be able to harmonise these three notes with the familiar pattern ii^7b–V–I since it ought to be possible to prepare the 7th (F) by using an F major chord at bar 2^2. It's appropriate to deal with this chord now rather than return to it later – in fact, you may find increasingly that you think in terms of *four*-chord progressions at ends of phrases – a cadence preceded by two approach chords. Here the chord before ii^7b *must* be I. Nothing but F could reasonably follow the leading note (E) in the bass on the previous quaver: not only does a leading note usually rise to the tonic, but the given chord of V^7b on this quaver nearly always leads to I.

Phrase 2 The melody ends with 1–2, suggesting an imperfect cadence in the tonic, I–V. The two notes before the cadence, F and E, also suggest I–V, but I–V–I–V for the complete progression would be rather dull. One solution would be to include an inverted chord and to use *viib* instead of the first chord V. This gives Ib–*viib*–I–V, which works well and offers more interest.

Phrase 3 Hopefully you spotted that this phrase can modulate to the dominant – always the most likely choice for a modulation in major-key chorales. The cadence itself is therefore V–I in C major, and this could be approached by either IV or ii to harmonise the F in the melody. The E at the end of the previous bar could be harmonised by chord vi (A minor in this key), but a tonic chord of C major might be more helpful in defining the new key of C.

Phrase 4 This must end with a perfect cadence in F major. Notes 3–2–1 can be treated as Ic–V–I, or as Ib–V–I, a more common choice with Bach (probably because the bass can be more active). To avoid using the tonic chord too many times, the F at the end of the previous bar can be harmonised with chord vi.

We now have the following skeleton harmonisation:

Ex. 1.15.2

3 Choose chords for the first part of each phrase, and write in the bass notes

Work forward from the beginning of a phrase until you reach the chords already chosen for the cadence and its approach. Make sure there is a good join between the last chord you now write and the approach to the cadence – be prepared to change any previously chosen chords if necessary.

The first chord of a new phrase must lead on well from the preceding cadence. Where possible, repeat the pause chord, with an octave shift in the bass (see the change to bar 3 in Example 1.15.3 *below*). It doesn't matter if this causes an overlap.

Here are reminders of several important points:

✦ I and $V^{(7)}$, and their inversions, are the most useful of all chords.

✦ Progressions in which the roots fall in 5ths (or rise in 4ths) are particularly strong. Chords with roots that fall in 3rds can also be very useful.

✦ Mix $\frac{5}{3}$ and $\frac{6}{3}$ chords rather than use many root-position chords in succession. The result is more varied, bass parts are usually less angular, and contrary motion between S and B is often easy to achieve.

✦ Modulations are usually best started early in the phrase, rather than left to the cadence itself. The cadence should merely confirm the new key.

With this advice in mind, try completing the remaining chords and bass notes. Compare your working with Example 1.15.3 *below* – but remember that there can be more than one right answer!

We've seen that the bass minim F in bar 3 has been moved down an octave. This is to allow the bass to rise to the upper F when the next phrase starts with the same chord. At the end of bar 5 we can't make a similar upward shift of an octave in the bass because this would take the bass part too high in the remainder of the phrase.

Ex. 1.15.3

F major: ⬩ I ⬩ ii⁷b ⬩ V ⬩ I ⬩ I ⬩ IVb ⬩ I ⬩ V ⬩ Ib

viib ⬩ I ⬩ V ⬩ V ⬩ IVb ⬩ I ⬩ F major: I ⬩ ii ⬩ Ib ⬩ V ⬩ vi ⬩ Ib ⬩ V ⬩ I
C major: IV ⬩ Vb ⬩ I ⬩ IV ⬩ V ⬩ I ⬩ IV

4 Add inner parts and check everything

Here are a few pointers to adding the alto and tenor parts:

✦ In bar 2 the given G in the alto ends with a tie. This G must continue under the soprano A, producing a 9–8 suspension against the bass F. The tied G will then need to resolve to F on the second quaver of the second beat. This F can then form the preparation for the 7th (F) of chord ii^{7}b on the third beat.

- ◆ The first half of bar 4 is very much like the first half of bar 2 – it would be a good idea to make some difference between the two, perhaps by making one of the inner parts in bar 4 different.

- ◆ In the last bar, you are likely to want a crotchet E in the alto on the second beat. This is the leading note and could then fall to C in the final chord, something very characteristic of Bach.

After adding the inner parts, check all six combinations of parts for consecutives. Be specially careful at the start of the final phrase – two adjacent root-position triads (I–ii), with outer parts in similar motion, are prone to consecutive 5ths. Try to ensure that the inner parts move in contrary motion to the bass at this point.

5 Add any further melodic decoration required

We can see from the given opening that this chorale, like many others, should contain quaver movement on most beats – although not on all, and not during the pause chords.

In the final working below, the opportunity has been taken to add several passing notes and some additional suspensions. There are additional harmony notes in the alto and tenor at the last quaver of bar 4; the simultaneous downward jumps of a 4th and 5th are rather awkward, but they do avoid the overlaps onto the next chord that would have resulted without them.

After adding notes of melodic decoration, always check that you have not introduced consecutives where there were none before.

Ex. 1.15.4

Example 1.15.4 is a completed harmonisation of the melody shown in Example 1.15.1. It is not exactly what Bach wrote, but it shows a clear understanding of Bach's musical grammar and style, and would achieve a good mark in an exam.

In the second half of bar 6, the dotted note in the alto means that D continues to sound against the chord of C on the last beat, creating a 9–8 suspension. The preparation, suspension and resolution (all in the alto) are marked P, S and R for reference – you don't, of course, have to label suspensions in this way in actual exam questions.

(a) Play and study Example 1.15.4 *opposite*.

(b) If you have access to a copy of *Riemenschneider*, compare Example 1.15.4 with Bach's own settings of this chorale – *R68* in F major and *R247* in G major.

You can learn a lot from comparing Bach's two settings with each other and with our own harmonisation here. *R68* and *R247* are both a bit more elaborate than would reasonably be expected in a chorale test – but remember that Bach is often more ambitious and/or imaginative than we can normally hope to be.

Why do you think that Bach found it necessary to cross the alto and tenor parts at the start of bar 5 in *R68*?

1.16 Practice tests in harmonising complete chorale melodies

The first two practice tasks are a little simpler than the exercises normally set in exams. The melody of the chorale in (a) is quite widely sung as a hymn in Britain.

(a) Complete the harmonisation of the following chorale melody. Remember to include some passing notes and possibly other types of melodic decoration.

Tip 1 The melody in bar 5 starts with the ascending scale pattern, 1–2–3. This is very common in chorales, and can be effectively harmonised with the progression Ib–viib–I. If the reverse of this pattern (notes 3–2–1) occurs *early in the phrase*, it can be harmonised with the same three chords in reverse order: I–viib–Ib. The contrary motion between S and B is excellent in both cases. This harmonisation is well worth remembering since it can be used in many chorales.

Musikalisches Handbuch, Hamburg, 1690 (adapted)

Tip 2 The melody of the final cadence in this chorale consists of another common pattern, the pitches 8–8–7–8. This is often harmonised with vi–ii^{7}b–V–I, since the 7th of ii^{7}b appears in the soprano, and can be prepared in chord vi and resolved in chord V. But vi–Ic–V–I also works. In this case it is the 4th of chord Ic that is prepared and resolved in the soprano. Try out both progressions.

(b) Complete the harmonisation of the following chorale melody, adding passing notes where appropriate.

The second phrase ends with 8–8–7–8 (notice the change of key) – reread the last paragraph on the previous page for ways in which to harmonise this pattern.

The ending of the third phrase could be treated as notes 3–2 in F major or notes 2–1 in G minor. Which do you think works better in this chorale, bearing in mind what follows in the final phrase?

Melody from Koch's *Choralbuch*, 1816

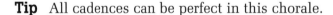

The tasks in Activity 1.16.2 *below* don't need to be tackled in a single sitting. They will test your knowledge of Bach's style of chorale harmonisation rather more fully. The final one is a little longer than most exam exercises.

Activity 1.16.2

(a) Complete the harmonisation of the following chorale melody.

Tip All cadences can be perfect in this chorale.

R6 (adapted)

(b) This chorale is quite short, but each phrase is unusually long. It passes through C major in bar 2, but is otherwise entirely in A minor.

(c) In a chorale melody the second of each pair of quavers is usually a passing note. However, the note marked * *below* should be treated as a lower auxiliary, and it is best to harmonise the two quavers at the end of this bar with separate chords.

Note the harmonisation of the soprano's minim D in bar 2. The chord on the first beat of the bar is ii^7 (whose 7th, A, is prepared in the tenor at the end of bar 1). As the soprano sustains the D, the chord changes on the second beat of the bar to V^7. Will this cadence, transposed to E major, work in bar 4?

There is a large-scale melodic repeat in this exercise. Aim for some harmonic variety in the repeated phrases (but avoid anything out of style).

(d) Complete the three lower parts in the following chorale. It is longer than you would normally expect in an exam question, so don't worry if you don't complete it all. There are also several tricky moments – here are some tips:

✦ If you are unsure how to tackle the cadences in bars 8 and 17, consider the possibility of imperfect cadences in C minor. These will work despite the preceding B *flats*.

✦ Unusually, Bach has a minim in all parts on the first note of phrase 7 (E♭ in bar 13), perhaps because the word in the text at this point means 'peace'.

✦ The quaver B♭ in bar 14 should not be harmonised separately – it is a non-chord note (an anticipation).

R215 (omitting last two phrases)

1.17 Tricky phrase endings

Most phrase endings in chorales fall into one of the common patterns we have encountered in this chapter. But occasionally you may come across other types of ending. To see how Bach treats some less common melodic patterns, play and analyse the cadences at the end of the following phrases:

✦ *R65*, phrases 3 and 4 each end with a falling 5th in the melody. Compare the same phrases in Bach's other setting of the same chorale (*R293*), and also look at *R332*, phrase 2, which similarly ends with a falling 5th.

✦ *R95*, phrases 1, 5 and 6 each end on the last beat of the bar with a repeated note in the melody. Compare these with *R128*, phrases 1, 2, 4 and 5, in which Bach uses repeated chords to harmonise falling melodic 3rds on beats 3 and 4 at the end of each cadence.

1.18 Chorale harmonisation in triple time

Although the chorales that we have dealt with so far have been in common time, with four crotchet beats in the bar, there are also chorales in $\frac{3}{4}$ time. However, the progressions and style of part-writing are essentially the same. There are three main points to bear in mind with triple-time chorales:

Chorales in $\frac{3}{2}$ time will *not* occur in Edexcel A2 Music.

✦ Sometimes the melody moves in a succession of minims and crotchets, with many of the minims taking a single chord.

✦ Passing notes below the minims are therefore crotchets rather than quavers.

✦ Some phrases may end with a **hemiola** immediately before the last chord of the cadence. This gives the effect of three minim beats in the space of two bars of $\frac{3}{4}$ time, and is most commonly seen when the prevailing pattern of | ♩ ♩ | ♩ ♩ | is replaced by a pattern such as | ♩ ♩ | ♩ ♩ | before the last chord of the phrase, as shown *below*.

Example 1.18 (i) illustrates all three of these points. If you compare it with (ii), you can see that working in $\frac{3}{4}$ time is otherwise no different to working in common time:

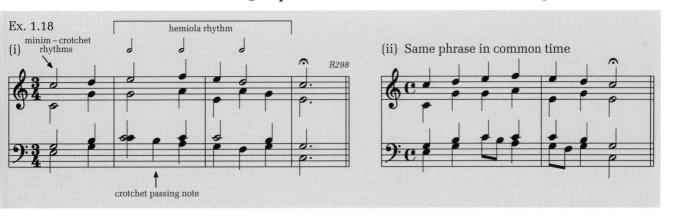

Ex. 1.18
(i) minim – crotchet rhythms
hemiola rhythm
R298
crotchet passing note
(ii) Same phrase in common time

Activity 1.18

(a) Complete the lower parts of the chorale at the top of the next page. While it would be possible to harmonise it all in the tonic key, see if you can introduce some variety by modulating to the relative minor at the end of the third phrase.

If you are confident in using them, try one or two secondary-dominant chords in the second phrase. Bach used V of vi and V⁷ of V in this phrase, again with the aim of providing some harmonic variety for a melody which employs the same rhythm in every phrase.

Chorales **35**

R334 (transposed)

(b) Complete the lower parts in the following chorale.

Notice that the final chord of the perfect cadence in bar 4 comes on a weak beat, contrary to common practice in most chorales. You will need to use a similar pattern for the cadence in bar 12.

R243

2   Baroque counterpoint

Counterpoint exists where two or more parts have simultaneous melodies with clearly distinct rhythms. The listener is more conscious of hearing different musical strands than in homophonic writing such as chorales where the parts are broadly similar (or occasionally identical) in rhythm.

We covered the basics of counterpoint in Chapter 5 of the *AS Music Harmony Workbook*, which you must work through before starting this chapter. Here we will look in detail at exercises in Baroque counterpoint which, for examination purposes, are normally based on music from the second half of the Baroque period (c.1680–c.1750). We shall learn about:

+ Figured bass (the symbols used by Baroque composers to indicate chords)

+ Adding a melody above a given figured bass and a figured bass below a given melody (as required for the Baroque counterpoint option in Edexcel A2 Music)

+ Completing two-part keyboard exercises (not involving figured bass) by adding a part to a given part (an option in OCR A2 Music).

If you are studying for the OCR option, you do not need to know about figured bass, but you should work through Sections **2.4–2.6** and **2.8** before turning to Section **2.15**, which deals more specifically with the OCR style of test.

2.1 Figured bass

A **figured bass** is a bass part in Baroque music which includes numbers and other symbols (such as sharp and flat signs) below the notes. These show the types of chords required, enabling a keyboard (or lute) player to improvise an accompaniment for other fully-notated parts. This process is known as **realising** a figured bass.

In practice, Baroque composers tended to rely on a player's ability to recognise what chords were needed from the bass part alone, and therefore often used figures only where there might be any uncertainty. In exams the bass is normally figured fully enough to show exactly what chords are required.

Ex. 2.1

Figured bass works purely in terms of **intervals above the bass**, using the scale of the current key. So, in Example 2.1 the figures $^6_4$ indicate that a 6th and a 4th above G are required to complete the chord, thus making a $^6_4$ chord of C major. The player has considerable freedom to adapt the realisation to the context, providing that the basic chord is correct. The notes may be put in different octaves, some may be doubled, the chord might be arpeggiated, and passing notes and other types of melodic decoration might be improvised to link a progression of chords.

2.2 Figured bass: using numbers

Baroque composers and players were so familiar with figured bass that abbreviated figuring was employed whenever possible. In particular, the figures 5 and 3 were not used unless needed for clarification. So, where a $^5_3$ (the most common type of chord) was required, no figures at all were shown unless accidentals were required.

Widely used figurings are listed in the table *overleaf*. The first column shows the abbreviated figuring, which is what you should normally expect to see. The second column shows the full figuring, and the third column gives descriptions and examples (all in close position). You don't need to memorise this table. Providing you know your intervals and keys, and understand how figuring is abbreviated, you can always work out the required notes directly from the figured bass part.

(nothing)	$\begin{matrix} 5 \\ 3 \end{matrix}$	triad in root position
6	$\begin{matrix} 6 \\ 3 \end{matrix}$	triad in first inversion
$\begin{matrix} 6 \\ 4 \end{matrix}$	$\begin{matrix} 6 \\ 4 \end{matrix}$	triad in second inversion
7	$\begin{matrix} 7 \\ 5 \\ 3 \end{matrix}$	7th chord in root position
$\begin{matrix} 6 \\ 5 \end{matrix}$	$\begin{matrix} 6 \\ 5 \\ 3 \end{matrix}$	7th chord in first inversion
$\begin{matrix} 4 \\ 3 \end{matrix}$	$\begin{matrix} 6 \\ 4 \\ 3 \end{matrix}$	7th chord in second inversion
$\begin{matrix} 4 \\ 2 \end{matrix}$	$\begin{matrix} 6 \\ 4 \\ 2 \end{matrix}$	7th chord in third inversion
4 3	$\begin{matrix} 5 \\ 4 \end{matrix}\begin{matrix} 5 \\ 3 \end{matrix}$	4 - 3 suspension with root-position triad
9 8	$\begin{matrix} 9 \\ 5 \\ 3 \end{matrix}\begin{matrix} 8 \\ 5 \\ 3 \end{matrix}$	9 - 8 suspension with root position triad
7 6	$\begin{matrix} 7 \\ 3 \end{matrix}\begin{matrix} 6 \\ 3 \end{matrix}$	7 - 6 suspension with first-inversion triad
6 5	$\begin{matrix} 6 \\ 3 \end{matrix}\begin{matrix} 5 \\ 3 \end{matrix}$	A $\begin{matrix} 6 \\ 3 \end{matrix}$ followed by a $\begin{matrix} 5 \\ 3 \end{matrix}$ over the same bass note. 6 5 does *not* mean the same as $\begin{matrix} 6 \\ 5 \end{matrix}$.
_____		A horizontal extension line means that the previous chord is still in operation, even though the bass note has changed.

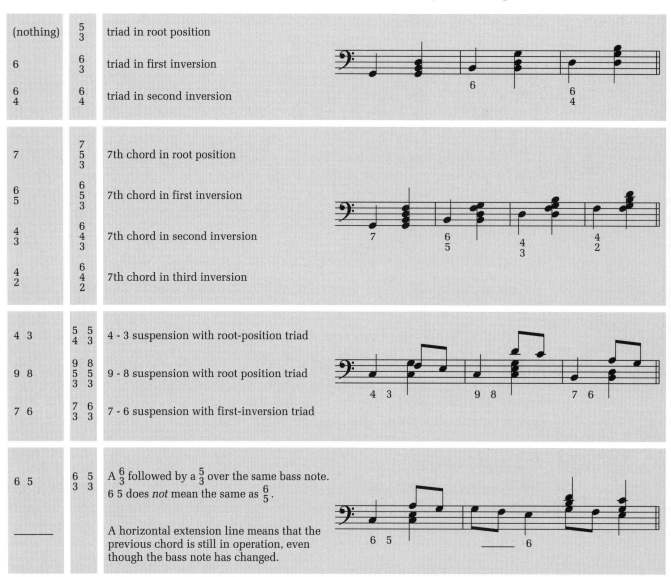

Activity 2.2

(a) Add figuring where needed under each of the following chords.

(b) Add notes above the following bass part to make the chords indicated by the figuring. The first three chords have been completed for you. Aim to give two notes to the right hand in each of your added chords.

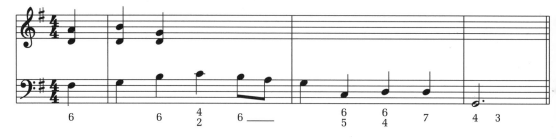

2.3 Figured bass: using accidentals

Figuring works in connection with the key signature. The first example *below* has no figuring, so it must be a $\frac{5}{3}$ chord on E. Since the key signature contains a G♯, the notes of this $\frac{5}{3}$ are E–G♯–B, a triad of E major. The second example does not have a G♯ in the key signature, so this $\frac{5}{3}$ must be E–G–B, a triad of E minor.

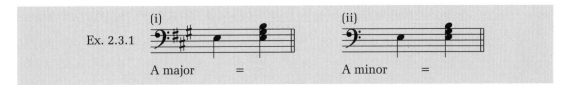

In order to change any pitches dictated by the key signature, accidentals are needed in the figuring. **An accidental by itself alters the 3rd above the bass.** So in the next two examples, the first chord is E minor and the second is E major.

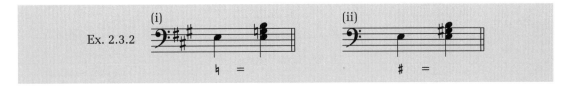

The most common use of an accidental is to accommodate the raised leading note in a minor key, as in Example 2.3.3 (ii) *above*, where G♯ is the leading note of A minor. If an interval other than the 3rd above the bass requires a sharp, flat or natural, the accidental should precede the interval number. For instance, in Example 2.3.3 *below*:

✦ ♭5 means that the 5th above the bass must be flattened, and
✦ ♯6 means that the 6th above the bass must be sharpened.

Note that in some printed music the accidental is written *after* the numeral (for instance, 6♭ instead of ♭6) and sharpening is indicated by a slash through a number – for example, ⑥ means the same as ♯6. Also, you may see ♯3, ♮3, or ♭3, rather than an accidental on its own, to indicate an alteration to the 3rd above the bass note.

Activity 2.3

(a) Write the correct figuring below the stave for each of the following chords.

(b) Complete a chord in close position over each of the following bass notes to match the following figurings. The first chord is given.

2.4 Two-part texture

A figured bass tells you which chords are required, but when you add a melody to a given bass, only one note at a time can sound above the bass part. Therefore you will have to choose suitable notes from the chords in order to create your melody:

- Where there is no figure the chord is a $\frac{5}{3}$, which means that you can choose a 5th above the bass, or a 3rd, or even an octave – **a 3rd is usually preferred**

- Where the only figure is 6, the chord is a $\frac{6}{3}$ which means that you can choose a 6th above the bass, or a 3rd, or an octave – **6ths and 3rds are both widely used**

Within these limitations, select pitches that will give a good melodic shape, and help you develop the style of the given material.

When you have to add a part above a figured bass, it may help to begin by writing down the available notes for each new chord the first time it appears, like this:

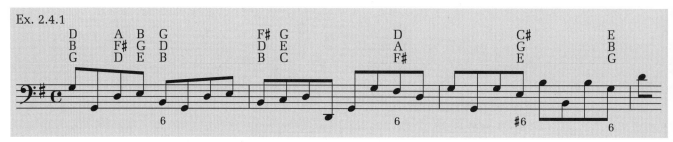

Ex. 2.4.1

Next, you need to select notes from these chords with a view to creating pleasing melodic shapes. Here, a rest has been used to separate the phrases, its position determined by the V–I bass (D–G) in bar 2^{2-3}, which can serve as a perfect cadence at the end of the first phrase:

Ex. 2.4.2

Finally, we can clothe this skeleton melody with some distinctive rhythms, which takes us to what the composer actually wrote: additional harmony notes have been added from the original chords, plus a passing note (the second A in bar 2):

Ex. 2.4.3

Telemann: Sonatina in G

As in most Baroque two-part writing, the majority of intervals are 3rds. There are a few 6ths (on some of the chords figured 6) and several octaves, but most of the latter are on weak semiquavers. An octave can sound too bare on the beat, although there is nothing better at the end of a strong perfect cadence to reinforce note 1. Too many 5ths, especially on strong beats can seem bare and ambiguous (neither major or minor). In Example 2.4.3 Telemann is happy to start with a 5th, but he wouldn't end on one. As Baroque composers often do, he uses a prominent 5th on chord V of the perfect cadence in bar 2^2, leading to an octave on G at the end of the phrase.

(a) Work out the notes needed for the chords in the following figured bass. Then add a melody in the same rhythm, choosing one note from each chord.

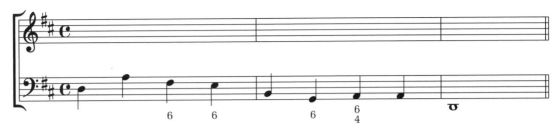

(b) Copy out the figured bass *above*, and then add *two* different notes in succession above most of the given notes. For instance, you might start with F♯–A quavers above the first note. Keep mainly to the notes of the chords, but add a passing note or two if you wish.

2.5 Melodic decoration

On the opposite page we saw how additional harmony notes and a passing note were used to give musical interest to the basic structure of a melody. Melodic decoration is an important feature of Baroque music. Patterns are formed from notes of the current chord (harmony notes) along with the following types of decoration:

✦ Passing notes (PN)
✦ Accented passing notes (APN)
✦ Auxiliary notes (AUX).

In the following examples, non-chord notes are printed in lighter type:

You are also likely to encounter:

✦ Anticipations (ANT)
✦ Échappées (É).

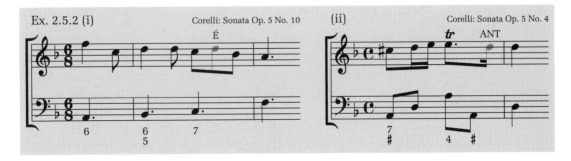

For more about non-chord notes, revise pages 54–61 and 73–75 of the *AS Music Harmony Workbook*. Note that it is best not to introduce appoggiaturas, since these may contradict the figuring. We shall discuss suspensions in the next section.

In Baroque counterpoint exercises you need not add any slurs, dynamics or marks of articulation (such as staccato dots) unless such things are specially requested or are printed in the given material – in which case, use that as a model. However, there is one symbol that is often worth including. When the melody at a cadence falls from 2 to 1, or rises from 7 to 8, it is very common in Baroque music for note 2 or note 7 to be decorated with a trill. A trill is just another type of melodic decoration, but instead of writing out the notes required you just need to add the symbol *tr* above the note concerned, as in Example 2.5.2 (ii) on page 41.

Activity 2.5

Using the abbreviations on the previous page, label each decoration marked *.

Corelli: Sonata Op. 5 No. 8

2.6 Using dissonant harmonic intervals

The types of melodic decoration outlined in the previous section are *not* shown in the figuring – they are for you to add. However, you cannot just choose to add suspensions or 7ths to the given chords – these accented dissonances *must* be indicated by the figuring. Remember also that **they must be prepared and resolved**.

Example 2.6.1 (i) *below* shows the correct preparation and resolution of a 7th chord (ii^7 in Bb major). In (ii) the 7th over the C has been neither prepared nor resolved and is therefore wrong. Part (iii) of the example shows the correct preparation and resolution of a 4–3 suspension, while (iv) shows the same suspension treated incorrectly, since it has neither preparation nor resolution.

Ex. 2.6.1

Including figured dissonances in your added part can be quite a time-saver. In (i) *above*, can you see how writing a 7th above the bass note figured 7 gives three notes for the price of one? This is because a Bb must precede the dissonant Bb (to prepare it) and an A must follow the dissonant Bb (to resolve it).

Sometimes it is impossible for the melody to reflect *every* figured dissonance. In the next example, the first 7th (G) has been included, but its resolution to F♯ gets in the way of including the second 7th (C) – it must be assumed that the player will incorporate the C in the realisation, perhaps as shown by the small notes:

Ex. 2.6.2

This activity is about the preparation and resolution of dissonances. Add the notes missing from the following passages. In passage (iii) remember that it is not necessary (or even possible) to reflect every dissonance in your added part. For instance, the given melody note (C) is not the 7th indicated by the 7 on beat 1, but since it is the 3rd of a 7th chord on A, it does not contradict the figuring.

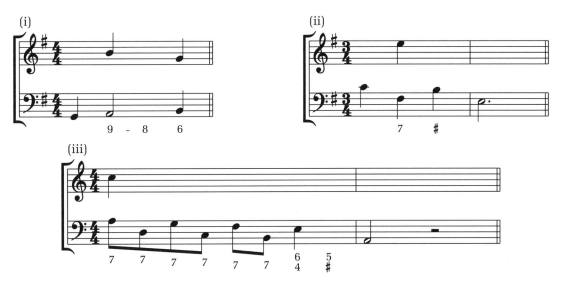

2.7 Cadences and modulation in figured basses

You might be tempted to think that figured-bass exercises are mostly about playing with numbers. It is true that you don't have to choose chords, but if you're to build a coherent melodic line you must know where cadences are implied and you must also be able to identify modulations, if only to know what accidentals are needed.

In early 18th-century counterpoint **the majority of cadences are perfect**. Many involve a drop of an octave in the bass from upper dominant to lower dominant, followed by the rise of a 4th to the tonic. If, in a *minor* key, the bass of a phrase, or even of a whole exercise, ends with a falling minor 2nd, the cadence is imperfect – specifically, that type of imperfect cadence known as **phrygian** (ivb–V).

Modulations are sometimes clear from accidentals in the bass part, but you must also look for accidentals in the figuring, such as the natural signs in the passage *below*.

Play the following bass. Name the modulation(s) indicated by accidentals on the stave and/or in the figuring. Locate and name the three cadences.

Handel: Sonata No. 4 in D minor

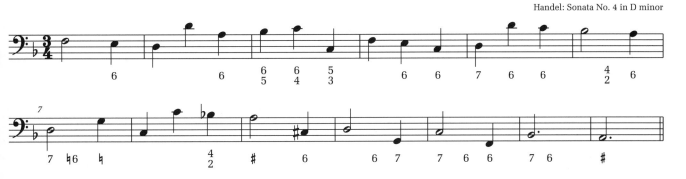

2.8 Imitation and the use of rests

Imitation was discussed on pages 66–67 of the *AS Music Harmony Workbook*.

Some Baroque two-part writing features imitation, although often not exact and rarely lasting for more than a few notes at a time. If you use imitation, remember that it must make good harmonic sense with the given part and not contradict the figuring.

Finding where imitation will fit is largely a matter of trial and error. It should sit easily with the metre of the music – for example, in $\frac{4}{4}$ time an imitative entry is much more likely to occur two or four beats behind or ahead of the given part than at three beats' distance. An imitative entry is frequently an octave, 4th or 5th above or below the other part, the object often being to emphasise notes 1 and 5. Both of these points are illustrated in Example 2.8.1 (i) *below*.

There may be rests in a given part when imitation is expected to occur in the added part, as in Example 2.8.1 (i). These help to highlight the imitation. Here are a few more tips on the use of rests:

- Never write a rest simply because you can't think of a note to write!

- Short rests (up to one beat) can occur at the same time in both parts, to help articulate the music (as in bar 2 of Example 2.10.1 on page 46)

- Rests longer than one beat are best avoided in an added part, except perhaps before an imitative entry

- When there is a rest in the bass between identical chords, the added part above the rest should fit with that chord, as in (i) *below*. If the harmony changes after the rest, the upper part may instead fit with the new chord, as in (ii):

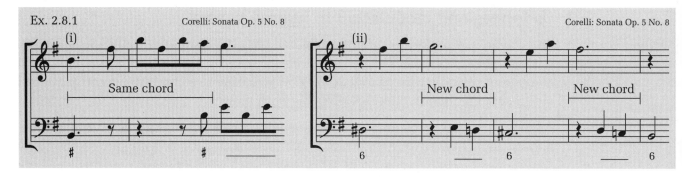

Let's see how an imitative violin part can be added to the following figured bass. It should enter at the start, since there's no point in beginning with rests in both parts.

The rests are a strong clue that when the bass enters it imitates the violin. If the violin starts with the bass melody an octave higher, the notes A–D will establish D minor from the outset by implying V–I. Imitation works up to the first note of bar 2, after which Corelli cunningly continues with the opening of bar 1, an octave higher:

(a) Complete the top part in the following, using imitation. Remember that the rests in the bass part (and the given rest on the top stave) provide clues as to where imitative entries may occur.

Thorley: Flute piece

(b) Complete the bass in the following, starting with an imitative entry of the bracketed figure in the top part. Begin by working out where the bass should enter and on what note. If you get this right, you should be able to keep the imitation going for several bars.

Corelli: Sonata Op. 5, No. 7

If you are taking the OCR exam you should now turn to Section **2.15** (page 68).

2.9 Introduction to the Edexcel Baroque counterpoint option

The Baroque counterpoint technical study for Edexcel A2 Music consists of a passage of two-part writing in which you have to complete missing sections. In some places you will have to add a melody to the given figured bass while in others you will need to add a bass (with figuring) to the given melody.

Both the melody and the bass will be provided at the start, to show the style and act as a model, and sometimes both parts may be shown briefly elsewhere.

You will be expected to maintain the given style in the material you write. While you do not need to know about the small differences of style between various Baroque composers you should aim to build up a broad knowledge of late-Baroque style by playing and listening to plenty of sonatas (and other music) by such composers as Corelli, Handel, Telemann and Vivaldi. (Since J. S. Bach is represented in the chorale option, his music is unlikely to feature in Edexcel's Baroque counterpoint tests.)

We shall start by adding a melody to a given figured bass, beginning in Section **2.10** with a limited range of figurings and fairly simple exercises, before tackling tasks more typical of Unit 5 in Section **2.11**. Later sections deal with adding a figured bass to a given melody and in Section **2.14** we shall look at working exercises in which both skills need to be used.

2.10 Adding a melody above a given figured bass (1)

Here is a working method:

Flute

Violin

1   **Note the instrument that has to play the upper part**. It will be either violin or flute. Although modern instruments have a wider range, in exercises of this type you should aim to keep your added part within the limits shown *left*.

2   **Identify key(s) and cadence points**.

3   **Make an outline for the top part** by writing in pitches and/or rhythms where they seem obvious.

4   **Complete your top part**, by adding to and elaborating your outline.

5   **Check your work** for consecutives and correct treatment of dissonances, and to ensure that you have observed (and not contradicted) the given figuring.

Play and study the following music, making sure you can hear the cadence points:

Ex. 2.10.1

Violin

Telemann: Sonatina II

Step 1   Violin is specified. Although a violin can play as low as G below middle C, a melody part in Baroque times usually stayed within the range from middle C to the D on two leger lines above the treble stave.

Step 2   The music begins and ends in B♭ major. It visits F major at the end of the first half and later passes through G minor (see the F♯–D–G pattern in the bass of bars 11–12).

We hear decisive perfect cadences in bars 7–8 (F major) and 15–16 (B♭ major). In addition, the bass outlines an inverted perfect cadence in bars 3–4 (Vb–I in B♭ major) and a perfect cadence in G minor (the pattern in bars 11–12 mentioned *above*).

Early 18th-century composers generally preferred not to over-emphasise a cadence in the middle of a section. So, although the 16 bars form a regular structure of four four-bar phrases, we'll try to keep the added part moving in bars 3–4 and 10–11 rather than let it come to a halt on a long note.

Step 3   The figuring gives much guidance for building a melodic outline, but also look for:

✦   Sequence or straight repetition in the given material

✦   Clues at points where the given sections of the melody end

✦   Obvious notes at cadence points.

Notice first that the bass part of bars 1–2 is repeated a 5th higher in bars 9–10. The top part should be transposed similarly – although it will link with bar 11 better if it is transposed down a 4th rather than up a 5th.

Now look for clues at points where the given material ends, and at cadences. We can:

+ Add D in bar 4 since the E♭ at the end of bar 3 is clearly a passing note – write the D as just a note head since we don't yet know how long it should be

+ Add B♭ to fill bar 16 – since it's always good to end a piece on note 1 when there is a clear perfect cadence

+ Add quaver rests at the ends of bars 6 and 10 to match those in bars 2 and 14

+ On the last two quavers of bar 15 the figuring suggests either D falling to C (which we've chosen), or B♭ falling to A (also satisfactory).

Now see if there's anything in the given material that can be recycled to help create a stylistically unified working:

+ Bars 13–14 can be adapted to fit with the bass and figuring of bars 5–6. This has the advantage that each of the four phrases can begin with the same rhythm set to different rising triadic figures. Starting on A in bar 5 will work, since it harmonises well with the bass, but starting the figure on F is also possible.

Here is the stage we have now reached, with the notes and rests added in Step 3 printed in lighter type:

Ex. 2.10.2 — Telemann: Sonatina II

Step 4 What we've added so far is very similar in style to the given material. We must keep this in mind as we work Step 4. We want the finished exercise to sound like one piece – not as if only parts of it are by an 18th-century composer!

Often the best way to fill a gap is by stepwise movement. An obvious example is the first note of bar 15, where E♭ can bridge the gap between F and D, and will harmonise with the E♭ in the bass. Don't worry that this leaves a bare octave on the first beat of bar 15 – this is not really a strong beat because bars 14–15 make up a hemiola (see Section **1.18** on page 35).

This leaves only bars 4 and 11–12 to complete. In both cases Telemann employed similar scalic figures, using melodic decoration to create stepwise movement. Look at bars 4 and 12 in the finished version *overleaf* and note the use of upper auxiliaries (E♭ in bar 4 and C in bar 12) and passing notes.

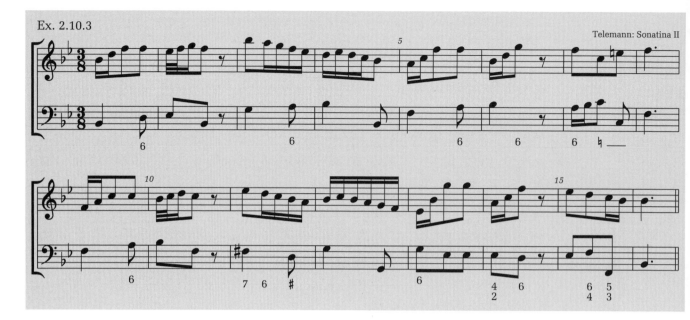

Ex. 2.10.3   Telemann: Sonatina II

There are three final points to notice in Example 2.10.3:

✦ The fourth note in bar 11 (B♭) is an accented passing note which briefly contradicts the figuring, but immediately resolves to A. Although such very brief on-the-beat contradictions can be effective, avoid them if in doubt.

✦ The unprepared 7th at the start of bar 11 is a rare exception to the rule about preparing dissonances and is best avoided in your own work.

✦ At the end of bar 15 there is a semiquaver anticipation of the final B♭. The anticipation of the tonic at a cadence after note 2 or 7 is a feature of Baroque style.

Step 5 After working an exercise, make a thorough check. Don't feel demoralised if, as a result, you have to revise parts that you thought were complete. It's all part of the learning process. Here are the main things to check for:

✦ Has the figuring been followed correctly, including the correct preparation and resolution of any dissonances?

✦ Does each note 7 rise to 8? Remember that:

   ✦ Note 7 can fall if it is part of a descending scale, as in bar 3 *above*, where A is note 7 in the key of B♭ major.

   ✦ The rise to note 8 may be delayed, as in bar 5 *above*, where the A doesn't reach B♭ until the first beat of bar 6.

   ✦ If you have studied chorales, the direct fall from 7 to 5 often seen in chorale cadences is *not* found in Baroque two-part counterpoint.

✦ Are there any consecutive 5ths and octaves? On-beat consecutives are easy to spot in two-part writing! Octaves or 5ths between *weak* parts of neighbouring beats do *not* count as consecutives. Telemann was happy with the octaves *below* because what we really hear is a sequence with parallel 3rds at the start of each bar.

Ex. 2.10.4   Telemann: Sonatina II

♦ Is the added part similar in style to the given material, perhaps even with some of the same melodic and rhythmic patterns, as occurs in Example 2.10.3 *opposite*? Be suspicious if your melody has a very different rhythmic character from the given opening. For instance, strings of quavers wouldn't have worked well in Example 2.10.3.

♦ Does each phrase of the completed melody have a pleasing overall shape? Many Baroque phrases are basically arch-shaped, with the highest note somewhere in the middle.

♦ Have you used a reasonably large part of the instrument's available range? The melody in Example 2.10.3 has a range of one and half octaves – it doesn't use the violin's low or high registers, but the range is enough to give the melody variety and interest. Melodies that mainly hang around the same few pitches are unlikely to sound convincing.

Activity 2.10

Here are some practice exercises to help you build on the work we have done in this section. In each one, complete the top part in accordance with the given figuring, and in an appropriate style.

(a) Write for flute in this exercise.

J. C. Fischer: Menuet No. 15

(b) This is a sarabande, with a characteristic emphasis on the second beat in many bars. If you include the 9ths in bars 10 and 18, or the 4th in bar 19, be sure to prepare and resolve them in your added part, which should be written for flute.

J. C. Naudot

(c) Write for violin in this extract.

Telemann: Sonatina VI

The figuring ♭6 in the first bar of the last stave *above* produces a first inversion of the triad on the flat supertonic, a chord known as a **Neapolitan 6th**. In the key of D minor this is a chord of E♭ major in first inversion (G–B♭–E♭). Put the distinctive E♭ in the melody, not the more ordinary-sounding B♭.

(d) The following exercise is for violin.

Handel: Sonata in D minor

2.11 Adding a melody above a figured bass (2)

The passage set in the Edexcel Unit 5 test is likely to include a wider range of figuring than the examples in Activity 2.10, and the style could be more elaborate, with a greater likelihood of imitation. However, you can still use the same five steps explained in the previous section.

Play and study the following music:

Ex. 2.11.1

Vivaldi: Sonata Op. 2 No. 8

Step 1 The top part is for violin. The lower part is labelled 'basso continuo' – a term commonly used for a Baroque figured-bass part.

Step 2   Remember to take account of accidentals both in the bass and in the figuring when identifying keys. For example, a glance at C major in bar 3 is signalled both by the figuring on the first beat of the bar and the F♮ in the bass during the second beat.

In bars 4–5 the presence of both F♮ and B♭ signifies a brief modulation to F major – can you see where the figuring indicates V–Ib in this key in bar 4? In a G-major piece, the appearance of F major is unusual – it is the subdominant of the subdominant, not one of the usual related keys. However, the key at the end of the first section (bar 7) is very much what you might expect.

The first half of bar 8 outlines a chord of G^7, followed by a chord of C major in the second half of the bar (with a suspended F♮ on the note decorated with a trill). The bass and figuring of bar 9 indicates that it should be treated in sequence, a step higher: A^7–D, with another 4–3 suspension on beat 3. These two bars don't really modulate – the two 7th chords are **secondary dominants**. The one at the start of bar 8 is V^7 of IV (in G major) and the one at the start of bar 9 is V^7 of V. Revise pages 47–48 of the *AS Music Harmony Workbook* if you are unsure about secondary dominants.

There are two very clear perfect cadences (in bar 7 and bars 13–14), each with the characteristic octave drop in the bass from upper to lower dominant below chord V.

Mark these cadences, and the other points covered in Step 2, on the score.

Step 3   Next we need to create a melodic outline. The exercise contains several sequences and these are a real gift where a given phrase can be recycled at a different pitch. This is the case in bars 7^4–8^3 – just transpose it up a step and write it into bars 8^4–9^3, adjusting accidentals to match the new context.

With some sequences you will need to be more inventive. For instance, you must devise your own violin part in bar 3 before you repeat it in sequence in bar 4. You may well spot other places that could be treated sequentially, although the figuring may dictate that they won't work without some variation in the melody.

Always look for clues in the figuring. For example, you could sketch in the 4–3 progression at the start of bar 13 (G–F♯). Remember that 4ths above the bass need preparation, so the G should also appear at the end of bar 12. The perfect cadences in bars 7 and 13–14 will probably end with the scale degree patterns 7–8 or 2–1.

Before continuing, make sure you have sketched in all of the melodic ideas suggested in the course of Step 3.

Step 4   Now fill out your skeleton melody to produce a complete version. Your melody should reflect the style of the given material, so there should be plenty of quaver and semi-quaver movement, produced with the aid of melodic decoration. Notice that the violin's notes in the given opening are entirely conjunct, apart from the leap after the rest in bar 1. This suggests that you, too, should aim for plenty of stepwise movement, but not all the time since there is a leap in the given melody in bar 11.

Step 5   Finally, check your work for consecutives, correct treatment of dissonances and consistency with the figuring, and the various other points listed under Step 5 on page 48.

The next example shows one possible working of this test. It is not as elaborate as Vivaldi's original, but it is a correct and reasonably stylish answer of the kind you should be aiming for. Notice the **octave displacement** on the first beats of bars 3 and 4, where a note is shifted an octave from its expected pitch to prevent the melody from getting too high – it is hardly ever necessary for the added part to extend more than about two octaves above middle C. Also note the imitation in bars 5–6.

Ex. 2.11.2

Largo

Violin

Basso continuo

Activity 2.11

Complete the top part in each of the following passages, in accordance with the given figuring, and in an appropriate style.

(a) Write for violin. Notice that there is imitation between the parts in several places and that the excerpt ends in the dominant key.

(b) Write for violin. The music is a sarabande, with the expected emphasis on the second beat in some bars. Most phrases are four bars in length, but their endings are not always obvious because the music continues through most cadences, as in bars 3–4.

Jones: Suite No. 1 (transposed)

2.12 Adding a bass part and figuring below a given melody (1)

In part(s) of the Edexcel Baroque Counterpoint option you will have to add a bass and figuring to a given melody. No bass instrument will be specified: just write a continuo bass line that would be playable on a cello. Keep your part mainly within the range shown *left*. It's acceptable to venture slightly higher occasionally, if there's a good reason, but don't go below the bottom C shown here.

When you add a bass part and figuring, follow the five steps listed *below*:

1 **Identify key(s) and cadence points**.

2 **Make an outline for the bass part** by writing in pitches and/or rhythms, and by adding Roman numerals for the chords, wherever they seem obvious.

3 **Complete the bass part**, by adding to and elaborating your outline. Continue to add Roman numerals for the chords.

4 **Add figuring under the bass part** in accordance with the harmonies implied by the given melody and your added bass part, taking account of any specific chords you noted in the two previous steps. Abbreviate figurings in the conventional way, for example by writing 6 rather than $^6_3$.

5 **Check your work** for consecutives, for correct handling of any dissonances implied by the given melody or added by you, and for accuracy of added figuring.

We'll now apply this method to the following short and relatively simple passage:

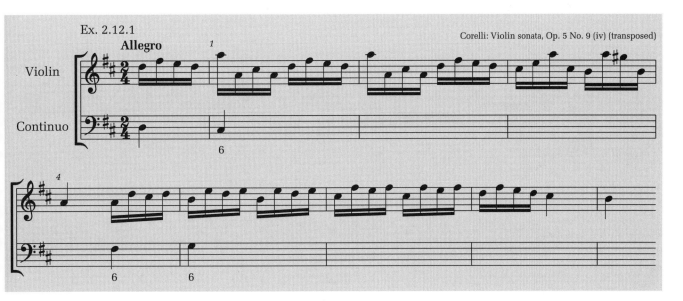

Step 1 The key at the beginning is D major. The G♯ in bar 3 suggests a modulation to the dominant (A major) and this can be confirmed by the crotchet A at the start of bar 4. This is also the first long note in the melody, suggesting that it is the last note of a cadence.

The crotchets C♯–B at the end of the extract form a second cadence, but they cannot be harmonised by any cadence in D major. An imperfect cadence in A major would fit, but **most late-Baroque music tends to be punctuated by perfect cadences** and here a perfect cadence in the relative minor (B minor) would work well.

Step 2 When beginning to build a bass outline, look for:

◆ Sequence or straight repetition in the given material

◆ Clues at points where the given bass part ends

◆ Obvious notes at cadence points.

Now we've decided on the cadences, we'll sketch in their bass notes and write in the Roman numerals. In Example 2.12.2 *below* we have included quaver movement in the bass at the end of bar 7 to keep the rhythm moving forward. This is not necessary with the crotchets in bars 4 and 8, since they are both final notes of a phrase, where a clean break from the mainly semiquaver rhythm of the melody is welcome.

Notice that chord V of A major will support only the last two semiquavers in bar 3 – a different chord will be needed for the two preceding semiquavers (bracketed in the example *below*). This means that chords will need to change on the quavers in the second half of bar 3 – **an increase in harmonic rhythm in the lead-up to a cadence is not unusual**, so always be alert for this possibility. The leap of a minor 7th in the violin part at this point suggests that a 7th chord will be needed and here ii^{7}b, a very common cadence approach chord, will fit well since the 7th (A) is prepared by the violin in the first half of bar 3, where the melody clearly outlines chord I of A major.

When figuring minor-key cadences, remember that at least one accidental will be required in the figuring for chord V (as is also the case for most cadences in passages that have modulated). Write these into the figuring as you plan the harmonies.

Turning to repetition, we can see that at the start, the first eight semiquavers of the melody are repeated exactly. Repeating the bass as well is tempting, but problematic because it would give the pattern C♯–D in bar 1, closely paralleling the C♯–D outlined by the violin two octaves higher. We'll reconsider these beats later.

The eight semiquavers in bars 4^2–5^1 are repeated a step higher in sequence, and here the bass could also follow them up the scale in sequence in a succession of first-inversion chords, as shown *below*:

Step 3   We now need to fill the gaps, taking care that what is added links well with material already completed. We can tell from the style of the given passages that the bass should be quite simple in order not to detract from the busy violin melody.

In bar 1^2 the harmony must support the notes D and F♯ (E can be treated as a passing note). We have already rejected a chord of D (crossed-out in the example above), but chord vi (B minor) would work. On the first beat of bar 2 the harmony must support A and C♯. We shall use chord iii (F♯–A–C♯) since it can be followed by vi in the second half of the bar. Alternatively, chord V (which is what Corelli used) would fit.

In the second phrase, we just need to add a cadence approach chord at the start of bar 7. D and F♯ are the obvious chord notes, leaving E to be treated as a passing note. A chord of D major would fit, but it contains an A♮ which will not prepare well for a cadence in B minor, so we will choose chord I of B minor instead.

A few improvements could be made. Bars 5 and 6 are rather dull – there is only one chord per bar, and the second half of each bar repeats the first half. Since we need to head towards B minor for the final cadence, we could make the second bass note of bar 6 an A♯, leading to the B in bar 7. And since bar 6 is a sequence of the previous bar, we similarly sharpen the second bass note in bar 5. The result is a chromatic ascent in the bass from bar 4^2 to bar 7^1, as shown *below*.

Step 4

There is further advice on figuring an exercise in Section **2.13**.

Here is our finished version, with the above improvements. The bracketed quavers in bars 3 and 7 are those used by Corelli to give rhythmic impetus to the cadence approaches. The one in bar 3 introduces a first inversion, and so needs a figure 6, while the one in bar 7 produces a new chord (E minor) on the second quaver of the bar. Corelli also added greater interest to the second beat of this bar by figuring a suspension at this point (shown in brackets below our own figuring).

Step 5   A careful check of the whole exercise shows that harmony, melody and rhythm all make sense, that there are no consecutives, and that all the figuring is correct.

Activity 2.12

Complete the bass part and figuring in the following passage, which passes briefly through the relative major in bars 4–5, and ends with an imperfect cadence in the tonic key.

Corelli: *La Folia*

The next example is a little more complex because, as in much Baroque music, the phrases are not of identical length and the cadence points are not always obvious:

Ex. 2.12.4

B. Marcello: Sonata in F, Op. 2 No. 1 (iv)

Flute

Basso continuo

Step 1   The key at the beginning is F major. E no longer seems to be a leading note by bar 4 – it falls to D at what is probably a cadence. The B♮s in bars 5 and 6 suggest C major, the dominant, confirmed by the final scalic descent to C.

If cadence points are not clear, begin by studying what happens at (or near) the end of two- and four-bar sections of the melody. The rest in bar 2 suggests a possible cadence on beats 2 and 3 of that bar – V–I in F major would certainly work well here. We have already noted that, two bars later, the long D in bar 4 could signify a cadence. An imperfect cadence in C (I–V) would fit the melody here.

The last four bars could be treated as a single phrase, ending with a perfect cadence in C major. There is no obvious cadence point in bar 6, although an imperfect cadence in C (such as ii–V) would harmonise beats 2 and 3 if you prefer to maintain a pattern of two-bar phrases, each with a cadence on beats 2 and 3 of their second bar.

Step 2   Look for the points listed at the foot of page 57. Here, bars 3^4–4^3 are a sequence of bars 2^4–3^3. A bass part descending in parallel 3rds with the melody works well the first time, and can be repeated a step lower for the sequence, although at bar 4^3 the root of a G-major triad (G) will give a firmer cadence than the 3rd (B♮).

In bars 4^4–6^1, a two-beat motif occurs three times in descending sequence. This passage can be harmonised as a circle-of-5ths progression: the flute's G and C at the start of bar 5 could represent chord I of C major, but an A in the bass (the root of chord VI^7) follows on better from the given E in bar 4. It also allows chord I to be reserved for the last beat of bar 4, where it can follow V^7 on beat 3 to help define the key.

Bar 7^2–7^3 can be treated as a repeat of the two preceding beats, as shown in the next example. The leap of a major 7th from C up to B♮ in the bass may look awkward on paper, but in context it makes perfect sense.

The endings of the given bass passages help us to:

✦ Add B♭ at the start of bar 2 – this provides a good link between the given A and the C we will need at bar 2^2 (the V of the proposed perfect cadence)

✦ Confirm the A at the start of bar 5 (which will be a 4th higher than the given E at the end of bar 4, forming the start of our circle of 5ths).

Bar 1 suggests that the bass will have plenty of dotted crotchets to support the busy flute part. The given quavers in bar 6 remind us that the bass should be more active where the flute has longer notes. The flute's rest in bar 2 can be matched by a rest in the bass to mark the first cadence. Usually it's better not to let the two parts rest simultaneously, but some Baroque pieces do have an opening phrase that is clearly separated by rests from what follows. Some quaver movement in the bass at the end of bar 3 will help to keep things moving when the flute is at its least active.

Step 3 There are just a few missing beats to complete in the bass. The imperfect cadence in bar 6^{2-3} could be harmonised as iib–V in C major, but this means repeating the F already decided upon for beat 1. Using ii–V for the cadence would allow a D in the bass, but Marcello actually wrote F♯, implying V^7b of V and providing chromatic colour in an otherwise diatonic passage. In bars 7^4–8^1 parallel 3rds between flute and bass work well, and provide effective rhythmic movement as the cadence approaches. At bar 8^2 a descending octave leap from upper to lower dominant would be very much in Baroque style.

Step 4 Since we have already planned most of the chords, adding the figuring should be straightforward, although of course it needs care. There is some detailed advice on working out figuring in the next section.

Step 5 Check that your added part makes sense harmonically, melodically and rhythmically, and make sure that there are no problems with consecutives and that all the figuring is correct. Here is our completed working:

2.13 Adding a bass part and figuring below a given melody (2)

When you worked Activity **2.12** (page 59), you probably discovered that the violin part consists entirely of chord notes, making the harmonies (and therefore the figuring) relatively easy to work out. In the previous section we learned how a knowledge of keys and standard progressions, such as cadences (with approach chords) and the circle of 5ths, can also help us decide on the chords to use.

Sometimes, though, the choice of chord is not immediately obvious. To discover the possibilities, remember that in Baroque two-part counterpoint:

✦ On-beat discords between melody and bass are rare, usually being limited to an occasional suspension. It therefore follows that the first of any group of notes within a beat is likely to be a chord note.

Once you have established the chord note(s), you can see how adjacent notes within the same beat relate to it. Those that are a step away are likely to be notes of melodic decoration, while those that are a 3rd away are likely to be other chord notes. In the next example the names of chord notes are printed below the stave, and the function of the other notes is shown above the stave. (PN = passing note, AUX = auxiliary note, ANT = anticipation and É = échappée.)

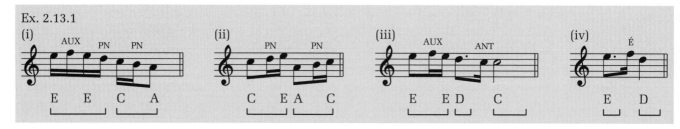

Ex. 2.13.1

There is no need to mark in the function of non-chord notes in your own work, but you may find it helpful to mark such notes 'N' as a reminder when planning your harmonies.

Non-chord notes *in the melody* do not require figuring when they occur on a weak part of the beat.

If you introduce a non-chord note *in the bass*, write a horizontal extension line under it to show that the preceding harmony remains in force. For instance, in the example *left*, the extension line shows that the opening chord (G major in root position) continues above the passing note (F) in the bass.

Suspensions

Non-chord notes in the melody that occur on the beat *will* need figuring. These are likely to be suspensions, and can usually be recognised from the characteristic pattern of a weak-beat note that is repeated on a strong beat before falling by step. The first and third of these notes must be treated as chord notes, while the middle one is the suspension. The first two notes may be tied, although often they are not, and the suspension may be decorated, as in (iv) below:

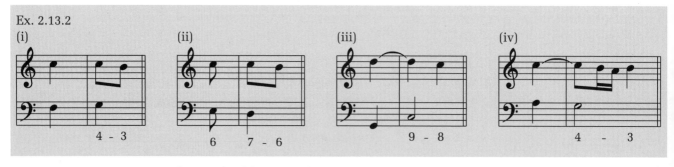

Ex. 2.13.2

Count the interval between bass and melody note to give the figure required for the suspension and remember that you must also figure the resolution, even if it is a note such as 3 that you would not normally figure. Octave differences should be ignored (so write 4-3 rather than 11-10), except in the case of 9-8, which should always be figured 9-8 rather than 2-1.

It is sometimes possible to figure a suspension even when there is not one outlined in the melody. This is usually done to add harmonic interest at a place where there is little movement in the melody, as at the end of Example 2.12.3 (page 59) where Corelli figures a suspended 4th in the continuo part. If you do this, remember that the chord before the suspension must include the pitch of the suspended note so that it can be prepared, and you must show the resolution of the suspension in the figuring. The effect of Corelli's figured suspension is shown by the small notes in the example *left* – the 4th above F♯ is B, which can be prepared as part of the first chord (E minor), sounded above the first F♯, and then resolved to A♯ above the second F♯ (as indicated by the ♯ sign beneath the last bass note).

7th chords

A 7th between bass and melody is a dissonance. When it occurs on the beat it is usually prepared and generally falls by step either directly or very soon afterwards, and so is effectively a 7–6 suspension, as can be seen in part (ii) of Example 2.13.2, *opposite*. The figuring for 7th chords is shown in the table on page 38. Remember that you may also need to show accidentals in the figuring. For instance, $^7_\sharp$ indicates that the 3rd of the chord needs to be sharpened.

Second inversions

A second inversion is figured $^6_4$ and should resolve by moving to root position triad over the same bass note, figured $^5_3$. The progression Ic–V is therefore figured $^6_4\,^5_3$ and this is the only time it's necessary to figure a root-position chord in full. Of course, some figuring will always be needed if any notes in a root-position chord require an accidental – for example, a ♭ by itself to signify a flat 3rd or $^{\sharp5}_{\sharp3}$ (often just $^{\sharp5}_\sharp$), meaning that the 3rd and 5th are both sharpened. The latter is often required when a minor-key passage has modulated to the dominant and chord V of the new key is used.

Accidentals in the bass

Because the bass note is never included in the figuring, any accidental that appears before a note in the bass part must not be figured.

Syncopation

Figuring is not our only concern. The rhythms of melody and bass should always complement each other – where one is slow-moving, the other needs more activity. In the next example, the melody has four syncopations, marked *. Note that:

✦ The bass part has an on-beat note at each point where the top part is held over, making the syncopation clear and effective.

✦ Each syncopated note creates a dissonance (a 7th or a 9th above the bass) at the point where it extends onto a new crotchet beat. The dissonance then resolves either immediately or (in the last two cases) after an intervening harmony note.

Ex. 2.13.3 — De Fesch: Sonata No. 6 (i)

Study this example carefully, as syncopated notes often appear in exercises of this type. Try covering up the lower stave and thinking about how you would tackle the harmonisation if you had only the melody to work on.

2.14 Exercises for Edexcel Unit 5

In the Baroque counterpoint option for Edexcel A2 music you will be required to add a melody to a given figured bass in some passages, and to add a figured bass to a given melody in others. You may find it easier to concentrate first on all the bars in which the melody has to be added.

Activity 2.14

(a) Complete the following in an appropriate style. Add the violin part in bars 3–6¹ and 13–14. Add the bass part, with appropriate figuring, in bars 8–11.

In bars 8–10 Marcello adapted the violin motif from bar 1 to form a bass part. You don't have to do this yourself, but can you see how it could be done?

Marcello: Sonata Op. 2 No. 1 (ii)

(b) Complete the following in an appropriate style. Add the bass part, with appropriate figuring, in bars 3³–7. Add the violin part in bars 8–12³ and 13–16.

Vivaldi: *Il pastor fido*, No. 2 (i)

(c) Complete the following in an appropriate style. Add the flute part in bars 3^3–7 and 14–17. Add the bass part, with appropriate figuring, in bars 9^2–13^2 and 20–22. There is frequent syncopation in this exercise. Try to introduce some syncopation in your flute part where the bass is unsyncopated.

We used hyphens between figures in exercises (a) and (b) to make it really clear where suspensions are used. From here on we've dropped them because in exam questions you have to locate suspensions without the aid of hyphens.

Handel: Sonata in B minor, Op. 1 No. 9 (ii)

(d) Complete the following in an appropriate style. Add the flute part in bars 3–6^3 and 15–18. Add the bass part, with appropriate figuring, in bars 8–13.

J. C. Schickhardt: Sonata, Op. 30 No. 6 (ii) (transposed)

2.15 Two-part Baroque counterpoint for keyboard (OCR)

This section is for those studying the Baroque counterpoint option in OCR A2 Music, a coursework task based on keyboard music that requires a number of exercises in which you add a part to a given part. Although the style will be similar in many ways to the two-part music encountered in most of this chapter, figured bass is not involved.

Your teacher will set suitable exercises, with both parts given in full at the start, to indicate the style. In these exercises the two parts may have similar melodic interest, or the right hand may have the melody while the left takes a mainly supportive role.

Two equal parts

J. S. Bach's two-part inventions are works in which both parts share the melodic interest. They were originally played on keyboard instruments of modest range. The lowest note is B, two leger lines below the bass stave, and the highest is C, two leger lines above the treble stave. The two parts do not cross.

Each of Bach's inventions is essentially a working-out of a small number of melodic ideas heard at the beginning. Bach's principal methods of development are:

✦ Imitation

✦ Melodic inversion (where a single part is turned upside down by reversing the direction of its intervals)

✦ Contrapuntal inversion (where the whole texture is inverted, the higher part becoming the lower or vice versa)

✦ Sequence.

Study and play the following passage and then follow the method for working this type of exercise described *below*.

Ex. 2.15.1   Bach: Two-part Invention No. 1

1   Identify key(s) and obvious cadence points

The music begins in C major. F♯s are in regular use from bar 4 onwards, suggesting G major, and the melodic pattern in bars 6^4–7^1 offers a likely place for a Ic–V–I cadence in that key. F♮ in bar 9 heralds a return to C major at the end of the extract.

2 Identify the principal melodic material and how it is used

The first seven semiquavers of the melody form a motif which is **imitated** by the bass in the same bar. The melody of bar 1 is repeated in **sequence** a 5th higher in bar 2 – the bass is likely be sequential, too. The opening motif is then used in **inversion** in bar 3 (marked with a bracket) and this version is spun out in descending sequence to fill the remainder of bars 3 and 4 – it also returns in bars 5 and 6, but this time only the last four semiquavers (marked with a pecked bracket) are used sequentially.

The melody from bars 1–2 returns in the bass of bars 7–8, transposed to G major, and the seven-semiquaver motif appears once more, in inversion, in bar 9.

3 Sketch in an outline of your added parts

Do this by putting in pitches and/or rhythms wherever they seem obvious, using the information gleaned in steps 1 and 2.

The melodic sequence in bar 2 gives the clue for completing the bass in this bar – it also follows in sequence, repeating the imitative entry of bar 1.

When the bass introduced the motif in bar 1 it was accompanied by quavers in the melody, which helped to give each part rhythmic independence. We can use quavers in the bass of bars 3–4, to accompany the continuous semiquavers, letting these harmonise the melody (in 3rds and 6ths).

Compare bars 7–8 with bars 1–2. Contrapuntal inversion of bars 1–2 can be used in bars 7–8. Try it for yourself, but look at the example *below* if you need to.

4 Complete your added parts and check your work

Example 2.15.2 shows the passage after adding the points in step 3 and filling in the remainder of the missing parts, with semiquavers where the melody has quavers or rests, and quavers where it has semiquavers. Finally, check your work, looking out for any forbidden consecutives and ensuring that accidentals are correct.

The working below is grammatically correct, but compare it with Bach's original to see how he derived nearly every note from the material in bar 1.

Ex. 2.15.2

Complete the missing parts in the following passage. There are plenty of sequences to help you here. The trill in bars 19–21 must be accompanied by some purposeful semiquaver movement in the left hand.

Bach: Two-part Invention No. 4

Melody-dominated keyboard music

In much two-part keyboard music of the late-Baroque period, the right hand has the dominant part and the left acts as a harmonic support or accompaniment. The style is often not very different from the two-part writing discussed in Sections **2.9** and **2.10**, starting on page 45, apart from the fact that the bass is not figured. You may find it helpful to read those sections, and to use the exercises (a) and (b) in Activity **2.10** for additional practice – just ignore the figuring in the given bass parts.

The method for working such tests is similar to that described earlier. First identify the key(s) and cadence points, then write an outline of the missing parts by sketching in the most obvious pitches and/or rhythms. Next complete the parts by adding to and elaborating this outline, and finally check your work.

Here is part of a keyboard movement by Bach. Study it and play it.

Ex. 2.15.3

Menuett

Bach: French Suite No. 2

Step 1   This is a minuet consisting, like many dances, of mainly four-bar phrases. Notice that the passage is 24 bars long (6 × 4) and that the long notes in bars 8, 16 and 24 all suggest phrase endings. Then, within these eight-bar sections, you'll see that bars 3–4 will support an imperfect cadence in the tonic (C minor) and bars 11–12 will support an imperfect cadence in the relative major (Eb major). There is no obvious cadence in bars 19–20, so the last eight bars will form one long phrase.

Bearing all this in mind, look closely at the given material, and then work out what all the keys are and what types of cadences will fit.

Step 2   The given material suggests that the bass will have quaver movement in those fairly few places where the melody is not in quavers. It can have crotchets and occasional rests elsewhere.

There is a clear use of sequence, especially towards the end, and bar 9 should be easy to complete as it seems to be a transposition of bar 1.

Given all this deduction, it should now be possible to dot in at least the first note of most incomplete bars, remembering that 3rds or 6ths between treble and bass are likely to work well. Add Roman numerals to show which chords you have identified.

Step 3   Decide whether each group of six quavers in the melody belongs to one chord or to more than one, and identify which notes are non-chord notes. For instance, the first four notes of bar 18 outline V^7 in Eb major. Perhaps the fifth note (G) is the resolution of that chord, implying chord I? If so, it may be difficult to decide how to make bar 19 sound harmonically fresh, since that seems to imply chord I. In fact, Bach treats the G as an accented passing note and the following F as a harmony note, so that the whole of bar 18 is based on chord V^7 and the whole of bar 19 uses chord I, with the C on the third beat treated as an appoggiatura. At this quite late stage in the draft working you should have something like Example 2.15.4, in which there is relatively little left to complete.

Ex. 2.15.4

Step 4 Try completing the remaining notes yourself – check your working and if possible compare it with Bach's original.

Activity 2.15.2

Complete the missing parts in each of the following pieces in an appropriate style.

(a) This is a little shorter than the 16–24 bars normally expected and only the bass needs completion. The bass pattern in bar 1 returns in one other bar, but elsewhere the bass can use either the rhythm shown in bar 3 or just crotchets and minims.

[Andante]

Marcello: Sonata No. 10

(b) This piece is in the style of a bourrée (a Baroque dance). The given sections of the left-hand part are entirely in crotchets – it would be possible for this type of walking bass to continue throughout the exercise.

3   String quartets

3.1 Introduction

A string quartet is:

+ An ensemble consisting of two violins, a viola and a cello

+ A composition, usually in three or four movements, for these instruments.

Quartet writing is
an option in A2
Music exams for
AQA and OCR.

In the type of exercise we shall study here, the part for violin 1 is given in full, along with the start of the lower parts to indicate the style. Sometimes a few later bars are also printed in full. You have to complete the parts for violin 2, viola and cello. As occurs in most exams, exercises are based on the simpler quartets of the Classical period, especially those from the late 18th century.

Both violin parts are always written in the treble clef. The viola part is written in the alto C clef, in which the middle line of the stave represents middle C. Unless you play the viola, this will be unfamiliar, so we will look at this clef in more detail *below*. Composers sometimes use the treble clef for unusually high viola passages, but it is unlikely you would need to do this in exams.

The cello part is written in the bass clef. Composers occasionally use the tenor C clef (with middle C on the second line from the top) for high passages, or even the treble clef for the very highest notes, but again this is not something expected in exams.

Typical working ranges for the instruments in string quartet exercises are:

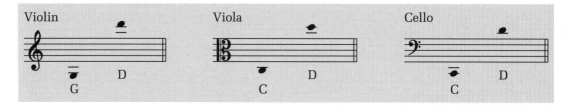

The bottom note shown for each instrument is the lowest note available, but you can go a little higher than the upper notes given *above* if there is good musical reason to do so. Although the two violinists use similar instruments, the part for violin 2 generally stays below that for violin 1.

The alto C clef Writing a viola part in the alto C clef requires great care, but it becomes easier with practice. The middle line of the stave is middle C, and it is useful to remember that the C below this hangs below a single leger line beneath the stave, while C an octave above middle C sits above a single leger line over the stave. Try playing the music on each of the following staves – they should both sound the same – and notice how the version in the C clef reduces the number of leger lines and avoids clef changes:

Ex. 3.1.1   Mozart: Quartet in C, K. 157 (i)

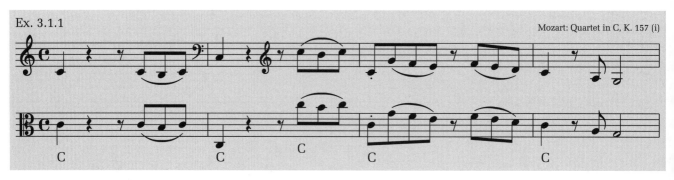

Score layout

A string quartet score always has four staves, one for each part. The staves are linked with a barline and straight bracket (not the kind of curved brace used in piano music) at the left end, and the barlines extend across all four staves. Tempo directions are written above the top stave only, but other performing directions should be written on every stave to which they apply:

Ex. 3.1.2   **Allegro**   Mozart: Quartet in C, K. 157 (i)

Ex. 3.1.3

It is tempting to sketch rough work for string quartets on two staves, with the two violin parts on a treble stave and the cello and viola on a bass stave. However, this is likely to result in an inappropriately low viola part – or else you have to squeeze the viola part onto the treble stave, alongside the two violin parts, making it difficult to see each individual line.

It is much better to work on four staves, but if you find the alto clef difficult, you could draft the viola part in the vocal tenor clef – a treble clef, with a figure *8* below to indicate that it sounds an octave lower. The opening of Example 3.1.2 with the viola part in this clef is shown *left*. If you use this method, you must transfer the part to the alto C clef for your neat work, but this is straightforward, just requiring every note to be moved down one step on the stave.

Articulation and dynamics

Example 3.1.2 includes an opening dynamic in each part, and a number of slurs and staccato marks. Always add slurs in your own working, using the given parts as a model. Where a rhythmic pattern is reused it will normally be played in the same way. For instance, if just the violin 1 part had been given in bars 3–4 *above* and you decided to add a part for violin 2 in 3rds below it, you would use the same pattern of slurs and staccatos as printed in the first-violin part.

Slurs should only last for a few notes, especially if the music is slow – don't add long phrase marks. If you want to slur consecutive notes of the same pitch, they must be marked with staccato dots (♩ ♩) otherwise the slur will be interpreted as a tie.

String quartet exercises may require other marks of articulation – chiefly accents (*sforzando*, etc.) and staccato dots. Again try to follow patterns in the given material.

You should also add dynamics. There are often fairly few in Classical string quartets, sometimes indicating little more than *piano* and *forte* contrasts. They are commonly the same in all parts, even where a first-violin melody clearly stands out as the main tune, so you can generally just copy whatever dynamics are printed in the violin 1 part onto each of the lower staves.

Bowing marks (⊓ for a down-bow and ∨ for an up-bow) were not normally used in Classical scores and should therefore *not* be added to your working.

(a) Write out the viola part of Example 3.1.2 (page 75) using a treble clef.

(b) Rewrite the following melody using an alto C clef. Then add dynamics, slurs and staccato marks in bars 5–8, following the model of the first four bars.

(c) Write out for string quartet the first phrase of the chorale on page 30, using four staves and with the viola part in the alto C clef.

3.2 Some basics of string quartet writing

Passages set for string quartet exercises are usually **homophonic**, generally with a melody in the first-violin part supported by distinctive accompaniment patterns in the lower parts. However, there is often an opportunity for a lower part to have a brief moment of melodic interest, as in bars 2 and 4 of Example 3.1.2 on the previous page, where the viola provides momentum through the rests in the other parts.

Although a string quartet exercise should be worked mainly in four-part harmony, one or two – or even briefly all three – of the lower parts can rest occasionally to provide a contrasting lighter texture. An accompaniment can sometimes support the melody better when it is quite light and not too continuous.

Double stopping

String quartets occasionally have more than four notes at once, for instance where the composer wants to strengthen a particular chord, as in **Activity 3.6 (f)** on page 92. This involves **double stopping** – playing two notes simultaneously on adjacent strings. The upper note of the pair must be at least as high as the note marked * *below*, because it is impossible to play two simultaneous notes on just the lowest string:

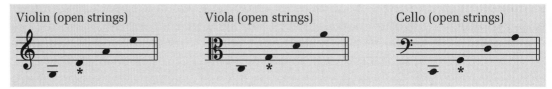

Double stops are easiest if one of the notes is on an open string (the notes shown *above*), but most intervals between a minor 3rd and an octave are possible, providing they are not too high in the range of the instrument.

If in doubt, you can usually avoid double stopping in your own work, or model what you write on given material. It is unlikely that you will need triple and quadruple stopping (simultaneous playing of three or four notes) for exercises at A2 level.

Style

Remember that string quartets are written for instruments, not voices like chorales and some of the four-part exercises in the *AS Music Harmony Workbook*. Repeated notes occur frequently (look at the cello stave in Example 3.1.2 on page 75), parts have a wider range, and there are usually more frequent (and wider) leaps than in vocal writing. Despite this, the two inner parts (violin 2 and viola) in simple quartets often move narrowly, and sometimes the upper or lower pair of parts will play in parallel 3rds or 6ths, as is the case with the two violins in Example 3.1.2.

Example 3.1.2 on page 75 illustrates several other features that will be useful when you work string quartet exercises:

✦ The **harmony is simple**, consisting of just tonic and dominant chords. Although more variety would be found in a longer passage, chords I and V$^{(7)}$, along with their inversions, were much favoured by Classical composers. Imperfect cadences often consist of the progression Ic–V, while Ic–V$^{(7)}$–I was often used for perfect cadences. It is an important point of style that Ic is used much more widely in Classical string quartets than in Bach's chorales.

✦ **Accented dissonances** are often used to add interest to the simple harmonies. For instance, the first F in the melody of bar 4 in Example 3.1.2 is part of a double suspension (F and D) heard over C and G in the lower parts.

✦ The **harmonic rhythm** (rate of chord change) is frequently quite slow – there is just one chord per bar in Example 3.1.2, compared with one chord per beat throughout most chorale phrases.

✦ **Periodic phrasing** (regular two-, four- and eight-bar phrases that balance and answer one another) is common. For instance, the melody in bars 1–2 of Example 3.1.2 is repeated sequentially to form bars 3–4, while the harmony of the first two bars (I–V^7) is balanced by the harmony of the last two bars (V^7–I).

3.3 Working a simple example

To work a string quartet exercise follow the five steps listed *below*.

1   **Identify the key(s) and locate the cadences**. Also label any given chords.

2   **Choose chords for each cadence**, including one or more approach chords, and sketch in suitable notes for the cello (the bass of the harmony). Remember that most cadences in Classical string quartets are either perfect (often Ic–V$^{(7)}$–I) or imperfect (often Ic–V).

3   **Choose chords for the remainder of each phrase**, and complete the cello part. A good cello part should provide a strong harmonic bass, and complement the melody rhythmically. Be guided by the given material, but remember that there will usually be some rests, where one of the other instruments will provide the bass of the harmony. The cello in a string quartet doesn't normally have the continuous movement of a chorale bass line.

4   **Add parts for violin 2 and viola.** In simple examples these may involve repeated notes and movement by step or small leap. In more complex writing they will probably be more agile and have greater melodic interest. Look for opportunities to develop distinctive accompaniment patterns, making use of the given material and/or creating new patterns. Make sure that leading notes rise by step to the tonic and that sevenths fall by step.

5   **Check your work**, watching out especially for mistakes in the viola part due to unfamiliarity with the alto C clef, and for incorrect consecutives. Make sure that you have included any necessary dynamics, slurs and marks of articulation.

For exam submissions, ask your teacher about any additional requirements for the paper you are taking. These may include labelling the chords with Roman numerals and inversion letters, identifying the composer and title of the work from which the exercise is taken, and adding the date when you completed the exercise.

We will now apply the five-step method to the following short passage taken from a string quartet by Leopold Kozeluch (1747–1818). Notice the slow harmonic rhythm, with just two chords in bar 1 and only one chord in bar 2.

Ex. 3.3.1   **Rondo: Allegro**   Kozeluch: Quartet in G, Op. 32 No. 2 (iii)

Step 1   The key is G major. The C♯ in bar 4 does not signify D major, in view of the C naturals in bar 3 and the lack of anything else to suggest a change of key. The C♯ can therefore be regarded as a chromatic appoggiatura. The grace notes printed in small type are ornaments that can be ignored when planning the harmonies to use.

As periodic phrasing is common in Classical string-quartet writing, locating cadences can be quite simple. Here there are two balancing two-bar phrases, followed by a more continuous four-bar phrase. The first phrase is already complete; we need to add a cadence at the end of the second two-bar phrase and at the end of the extract.

Step 2   We can see from the given opening that there is only one chord in bar 2, and so only one is needed at the comparable place in bar 4. The first chord of the cadence will therefore need to go in the second half of bar 3, and the second chord in bar 4. We have already decided that C♯ in bar 4 is melodic decoration, so the harmony notes in that bar are A and D, which can be harmonised by chord V – in other words, this will be an imperfect cadence. In bar 3, chord I will fit the two Bs, leaving A to function as a lower auxiliary note. Using chord I here will also follow on well from the given V⁷c on the first beat of bar 3. Incidentally, Classical composers liked V⁷c almost as much as other inversions of V⁷, whereas Baroque composers use it quite rarely.

The extract ends on the note A, which cannot be harmonised with a tonic chord, so we will need another imperfect cadence to end the exercise. The last two notes in the first-violin part are B–A. When, as here, a phrase ends with the pitches 3–2 of the scale, *moving from a strong beat to a weaker one*, Classical composers almost always harmonised them with Ic–V.

78 String quartets

On page 92 of the *AS Music Harmony Workbook*, we learned that Ic–V is essentially an embellishment of chord V, so to make the cadence we need another chord to place in the second half of bar 7. The notes to harmonise here are E and C, so chord IV would work well. Chord ii (A, C and E) is another possibility, but in straightforward Classical writing, the primary triads (I, IV and V) are often sufficient. An approach chord to our imperfect cadence (IV–Ic–V) could sit under the G and B in the first half of bar 7. We will use I here, although vi (E, G and B) might seem possible instead.

Pencil in as noteheads rather than precise note values, the bass notes we've so far worked out, and label the chords.

Step 3 Bar 6 contains a similar melody to bar 5; the same chords will work both times. The given B in the bass of bar 5 can therefore be pencilled into the start of bar 6 and be labelled with the same chord (Ib) given at the start of bar 5.

The three-quaver pattern (A–F♯–D) in these two bars outlines a dominant triad. Trial and error will show that V^7d, the last inversion of the dominant 7th, is the only form of $V^{(7)}$ that will harmonise these notes well. $V^{(7)}$ in root position gives a bumpy bass line. $V^{(7)}$b won't work, because the leading note (F♯) would be in the bass, and couldn't rise to G (because we've already decided that the next bass note will be B). $V^{(7)}$c, with bass note A, would give consecutive octaves with violin 1.

Using V^7d means that the 7th of the chord (C) will be in the bass. It cannot be prepared, but it is approached logically enough by step from B and duly resolved. Classical composers often didn't prepare the 7th of V^7 but they were just as careful to *resolve* it as they were to resolve any other dissonance. For this reason, the first bass note of bar 7 must be B, since it is the note of resolution – we cannot use vi here, as seemed possible when we were working Step 2.

Note that the 7th in ii^7 is normally prepared in music of this period.

Our draft of the cello part and harmony now looks like this:

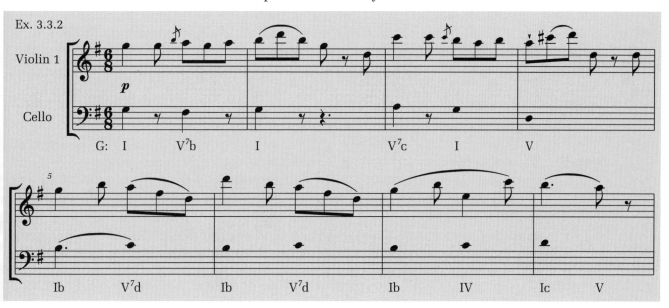

Ex. 3.3.2

Having completed our outline cello part, we must decide on precise note values. Bars 5–7 will sound dull if we write just a series of dotted crotchets. Kozeluch achieved variety by speeding up the harmonic rhythm in bar 7 (as Classical composers often do before an important cadence), using four chords in the same rhythm as violin I, namely Ib–I–IV–ii, instead of the I–IV progression sketched in *above*. (We've incorporated Kozeluch's version into Example 3.3.3, *overleaf*.)

Step 4 In a straightforward piece like this, violin 2 and viola can be simple filling-in parts, completing the harmony without fuss. Sustained or repeated notes (as implied by the given material in bar 5) and stepwise movement are sufficient almost all the time.

Example 3.3.3 *below* shows a completed working of Example 3.3.1. The leading-note doublings in bars 5–6 are so well covered that they don't count as faults. Kozeluch's original differs from our working in several ways – but remember that the object of an exercise such as this is to show what you know about Classical harmony and quartet writing rather than to guess at what the composer actually wrote.

Ex. 3.3.3   **Rondo: Allegro**

Step 5   A careful check reveals that all is well. There are no dynamics in the given melody after bar 1 that need copying into the other parts, and the solitary articulation mark in bar 4 is part of a melodic figure that doesn't occur elsewhere. The melody in the second half of the exercise is more continuous than in the first half, reflected by the slurs in the given melody. We have therefore used either slurred pairs of dotted crotchets in the lower parts to match this, or dotted minims where a part can stay on the same pitch throughout a bar.

Summary   Our accompaniment is light and compact, with a fairly high cello part, and all three lower parts are close together. The melody stands out well partly because it keeps high above the other instruments. Although this means that the first-violin part is more isolated from the accompaniment than is usual in simple quartet textures, there is no need for neighbouring upper parts in a string quartet to keep within an octave of each other, as in chorales.

There are a number of rests in the first half of the extract, reflecting the style of the given opening. In particular, the **anacruses** (upbeats) at the ends of bars 2 and 4 are left unharmonised. This is common in quartets (and most music) of the Classical period and is a point to remember when you work on your own exercises.

(a) Complete the following passage from a string quartet by Kozeluch. It can be harmonised with just chords I, IV, V^7 and vi in root position, plus Ic, although you can include other chords if you wish.

The second violin and viola parts could have the same rhythmic pattern in every full bar. The cello's double stopping at the end emphasises the new *forte* marking, but there is no need to use any double stopping in your added parts.

(b) Complete the string parts in the passage printed on the next page. Notice the difference between the sustained harmony in the quiet first half, where you should aim to use slurred crotchets or minims, and the more lively repeated quavers that begin in bar 9 to accompany the louder second half.

As we saw in Example 3.1.2 (page 75), Classical composers often based four-bar phrases on the progression I–$V^{(7)}$–$V^{(7)}$–I, usually with some inversions. The pattern is often found at the start of a movement where it is used to establish the key. In this exercise it could be used in bars 1–4 and again, if you wish, in bars 9–12.

Look out for melodic figures that suggest chords, such as those shown *left*. The modified sequence in bars 5–6 could be harmonised with four chords from a circle-of-5ths progression providing you avoid consecutive octaves in the outer parts between bar 4^2 and bar 5^1. The phrase starting in bar 12^2 is a varied repeat of the phrase starting in bar 4^2 and could be harmonised similarly, although it should be accompanied by quavers, not crotchets or minims.

String quartets **81**

3.4 Triple suspensions

Before moving on to more advanced examples, we'll revise a resource that we encountered on page 74 of the *AS Music Harmony Workbook* – the **triple suspension**. In a perfect cadence, Classical composers often prolonged notes from chord V^7 at the moment when the bass part (alone) moved to the root of chord I, like this:

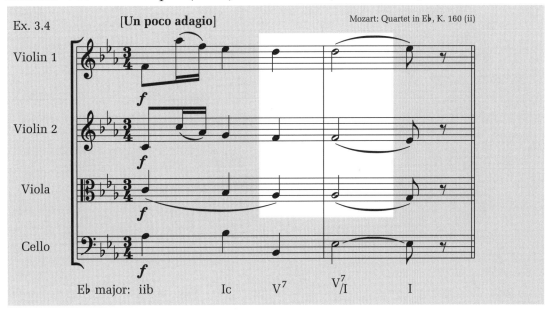

All three upper notes of chord V^7 (shown with a white background) are suspended into the final bar, while the cello sounds the tonic (E♭). On the final quaver, the three upper parts then resolve to notes of the tonic chord (the first violin unusually resolves *upwards* because D is the leading note and therefore has to rise to the tonic).

A triple suspension is such a common feature of the Classical style that it is worth looking out for perfect cadences in which the melody ends with this characteristic stepwise lean onto a note of the tonic chord, either from above or below. It won't usually work to suspend only one or two notes of chord V^7 when you see this pattern – all three upper notes of the chord need to be suspended. Notice that chord I in the example *above* has three roots and a 3rd, but no 5th. This is common with triple suspensions – if you want to include the 5th in the tonic chord, it will require a double stop in one of the parts.

Activity 3.4

Complete the following, to end with a triple suspension over a perfect cadence.

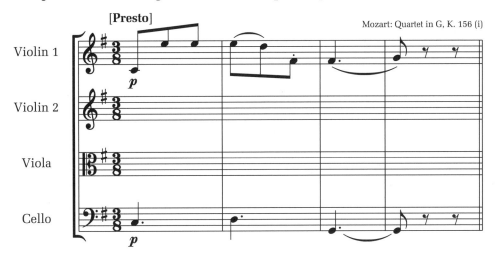

3.5 More advanced examples

The following passage takes us beyond the simple styles we have seen so far and, for the first time in this chapter, introduces a minor key. Only the first-violin part is given from bar 3 onwards.

Ex. 3.5.1

Kozeluch: Quartet Op. 33 No. 2 (ii)

Step 1   We can tell that the key is A minor from the absence of a key signature, the G♯s in the given parts and the chord of A minor at the start of bar 1. We are still in that key in bar 4, where the quaver rest signals a phrase break after a cadence.

This is the beginning of a regular pattern – our exercise has four four-bar phrases, each ending with a quaver rest.

In the second phrase, G is not sharpened in bar 7. This, along with the give-away arpeggiation of a chord of C major in that bar, leaves no doubt that this phrase ends with a perfect cadence in C, the relative major, in bar 8.

Phrase 3 begins with another C major outline but, after a short chromatic ascent, it ends on D in bar 12. The presence of both C♯ and B♭ indicate that the cadence in this bar should be in D minor, the subdominant key.

The final phrase ends in A minor. The notes on the two main beats of bar 16 are G♯ and B, both of which come from chord V of A minor, not chord i, so the extract will need to finish with an imperfect cadence.

Step 2   The first cadence must be imperfect because the notes on the two main beats of bar 4 (G♯ and B) both belong to chord V of A minor. Given the leisurely harmonic rhythm of the given opening, the first chord of this cadence will need to go in the second half of bar 3, where chord *iib* will harmonise the given B (the quaver A can be treated as a passing note). The first violin helpfully outlines all the notes of chord i in the first half of this bar, so we can plan the harmony of bars 3–4 as | i *iib* | V |.

We decided that the second cadence is in C major, and the repeated B from bar 7 to bar 8 suggests that it could be a V^7–I perfect cadence with triple suspension. The arpeggiation in the first half of bar 7 spells out chord I of C. To avoid anticipating the root-position tonic chord in the cadence, we will use Ic as the approach chord, which results in a progression for bars 7–8 that is highly characteristic of the Classical style: | Ic V^7 | I (with triple suspension) |.

Ex. 3.5.2
échappée

iv ____ V^7

The melodic pattern in bar 12 echoes that of bar 8. It will be fine to use a perfect cadence with triple suspension again here, since the key of D minor at this point will ensure that the cadence doesn't sound repetitive. Chord V^7 doesn't obviously fit the second half of bar 11, unless the violin D is treated as a suspension with a delayed resolution to C♯ at the end of the bar. We've opted for the simpler solution shown *left*, in which the semiquaver E is treated as an échappée.

The last phrase ends like the first (the violin part of bar 16 is an octave transposition of bar 4), and chord V can again be used throughout the last bar. The first chord of this cadence can't be *iib*, as it was in bar 3, since this won't fit the melody of bar 15. It shouldn't be Ic, either, because this would result in Ic–V sounding from weak to strong, instead of the usual strong to weak. Ib followed by I would work, but seems a little dull. Instead, we have chosen to use the progression VI–iv–I–Ib for bar 15, in the rhythm ♩ ♪♩ ♪. A more active harmonic rhythm is often used before a cadence, and in the final working (*overleaf*) you will see that we have used a similar harmonic rhythm in bar 11, leading into the third cadence.

Step 3 The B at the end of bar 4 could be unharmonised, like the initial anacrusis, although our version has G♯ in the second violin, anticipating the parallel 3rds between violins that we shall use in bar 5. Only two chords are needed in bar 5 (i and iv), reflecting the slow harmonic movement at the start of the first phrase, but we've used more variety in bar 6, on the approach to the second cadence.

The opening three notes of phrase 3 invite chord I of C major at the start of bar 9, just as the opening three notes of phrase 1 point to chord I of A minor in the first complete bar. The G♯ at the end of bar 9 is chromatic, but it leads to a long A in bar 10 that could be harmonised with a chord of A minor. However, A *major* makes better sense here because the music is modulating towards D minor, and A major is chord V of that key. One plain chord throughout bar 10 would sound dull, so we've introduced a 4–3 suspension to maintain harmonic interest.

Phrase 4 begins by outlining a D minor chord. The first two semiquavers at the end of bar 12 can be left unharmonised, to match the opening anacrusis of the exercise, leaving the lower parts to enter with the chord at the start of bar 13. We need to start modulating back towards A minor in this phrase, so we have used chord ib of that key in the second half of bar 13, allowing us to reintroduce C♮ in the cello part.

Step 4 The part-writing in the completed working (on the next page) is straightforward. The parts do not cross and the middle two contain small intervals, but there is a reasonable amount of rhythmic interest, helped by the use of passing notes. We have also acted on clues from the given material: compare the violin parts in 3rds in bars 5 and 1, and note the use of the opening dotted rhythm in the viola part of bars 7 and 10.

Step 5 Check your work, taking special care over accidentals when working in minor keys, and ensuring that all pitches in the alto C clef are as you intend. Remember to include dynamics, slurs and marks of articulation in your added material.

Ex. 3.5.3

Activity 3.5

(a) Study the following first-violin part, and identify the key and type of cadence to use at each of the places indicated.

The first answer has been completed for you. Notice the position of this cadence. Although it may not seem to be in an obvious place, it comes at the end of a phrase that lasts 16 crotchets (i.e. the equivalent of four bars), which is what we should expect in the Classical style. The start of a new phrase in the second half of bar 4 is made clear by a change of dynamic and a leap to a higher range.

The harmony notes in bar 4 are marked 'H' – they are part of a chord of D major, which is chord V in G major, and explains why the first cadence is imperfect. If the G in this bar was a harmony note, the F♯ that follows it would have to be a passing note – but it cannot be, because F♯ is followed by a leap. It must therefore be a harmony note. Always be alert for clues of this kind!

Finally, look out for the sequential repetition of bars 16^3–18^2 in bars 18^3–20^2.

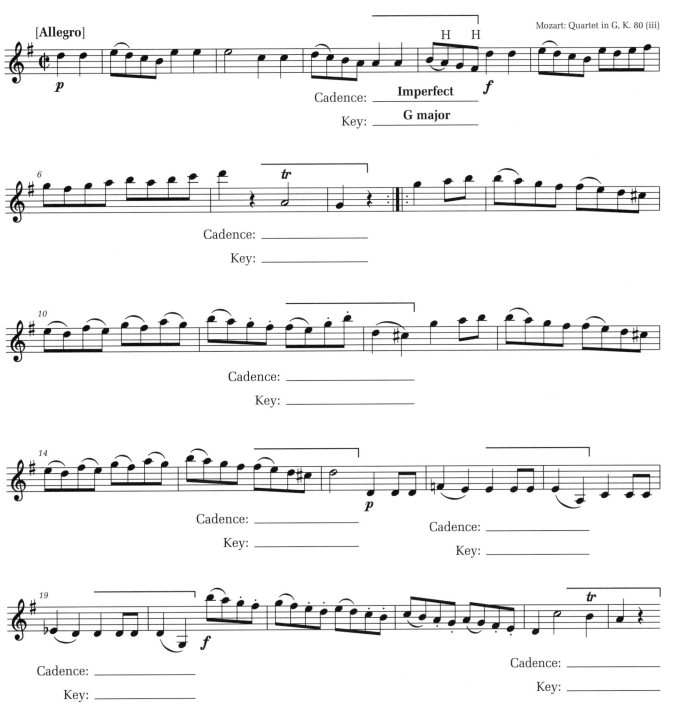

(b) Study the following first-violin part, and identify the key and cadence to use at each of the places indicated. The first answer has been completed for you.

The C♯s in bars 14 and 16, and the E♮s in bars 18 and 20 should be regarded as chromatic lower auxiliary notes rather than as signs of modulation. The F♮ in bar 16, on the other hand, is a clue that one of the lower parts must have had an F♯ earlier in this bar.

Schubert: Quartet in G minor D. 173 (iv)

Cadence: __Imperfect__
Key: __G minor__

Cadence: _____
Key: _____

Cadence: _____
Key: _____

Cadence: _____
Key: _____

Cadence: _____
Key: _____

(c) Complete the lower parts in the following passage. All four parts are in octaves in bar 5. It is not uncommon to find *short* passages in octaves like this (or to see a first-violin melody doubled an octave lower by the second violin), but avoid octaves in your own work *unless* the given material strongly suggests their use.

Although this exercise is quite long, some bars can be treated as repeats (or varied repeats) of earlier bars. The first-violin part in bars 17–21 moves more slowly than elsewhere, so include some shorter notes in the lower parts (perhaps using the dotted rhythm from bar 1) to maintain rhythmic interest. Try to reflect the first violin's rising sequence in your added parts in these bars. Reread the last two sentences on page 78 for a hint on how best to harmonise the final cadence.

Vanhal: Quartet in C minor, Op. Post.

(d) Complete the lower parts in the following passage. The given parts suggest that a number of rests can be used in the accompaniment. The final cadence will work best if the F♯ in bar 17 is treated as an appoggiatura – in other words, look for a chord to harmonise E, not F♯, on the last beat of bar 17.

Vanhal: Quartet Op. 13 No. 2 (iii)

(e) Complete the following passage from a minuet by Haydn, the most original and most prolific of all 18th-century composers of string quartets. Note the harmonic tension of the opening, with its diminished-7th chord in bar 2. There is an opportunity for you to use a diminished-7th chord in a different key, near the end. If you wish, you could follow Haydn in writing for just the three upper parts in bars 15–16 to help reflect the reduction to *piano* here.

Menuetto

Haydn: Quartet Op. 9 No. 4 (ii)

(f) Complete the following passage from a quartet by Mozart. Make sure you are clear about the keys used, and note that there are some accented dissonances, including the first semiquaver of bar 11 (chromatic) and the first semiquaver in bar 21.

Mozart exploits parallel 3rds between neighbouring parts in a big way in bars 1–2, and he reinforces the *p* dynamic in bars 11–12 and 17 by reducing the texture to just two parts. Bar 26 is really just a link between sections – as often with linking passages, Mozart leaves the melody in this bar completely unharmonised.

4 Popular songs

This chapter is intended for those taking the Edexcel A2 Technical Study entitled Popular Song. Section 4.6, on writing a bass part, should also be useful for students studying the OCR Stylistic Techniques option of the same name.

4.1 What the Edexcel task requires

The Edexcel Popular Song option requires you to add a bass-guitar part plus chord symbols to a given treble-clef melody in part(s) of the exercise, and a melody in the treble clef plus chord symbols to a given bass-guitar part elsewhere in the exercise.

Examination questions will be in ballad-song style, with a lyrical melody suitable for singing (although no lyrics will be given). The harmonic vocabulary expected will be varied and quite extended, with chords usually changing at least once per bar and going well beyond the simple I, IV and V patterns associated, for example, with the 12-bar blues. The exercise will include one or more changes of key.

The music will be commissioned specifically for the exam, and will not be closely associated with any particular style. Nevertheless, you will find it useful to explore songs by such writers as Elton John, Billy Joel and Carol King.

4.2 Chord symbols

We begin with chord symbols, the most straightforward way into the task. They are used to indicate the harmonies on which the accompanying players build their parts. Here is a summary of the symbols you are likely to come across in the given passages of a question.

- A note name by itself means a major triad on that note:
  G = G major (G B D)   **B♭** = B♭ major (B♭ D F)

- A note name followed by **m** means a minor triad on that note:
  Gm = G minor (G B♭ D)   **F♯m** = F♯ minor (F♯ A C♯)

- A note name followed by **dim** means a diminished triad on that note:
  Gdim = G diminished (G B♭ D♭)   **C♯dim** = C♯ diminished (C♯ E G)
  You may find it easiest to think of a diminished triad as a minor triad changed to have a diminished 5th, not a perfect 5th, above the root.

- A note name followed by ^{7} means a major triad plus a minor 7th from the root:
  G^7 = G 7th (G B D F)   **E♭^{7}** = E♭ 7th (E♭ G B♭ D♭)

- A note name followed by **m^7** means a minor triad plus a minor 7th from the root:
  Gm^7 = G minor 7th (G B♭ D F)   **F♯m^7** = F♯ minor 7th (F♯ A C♯ E)

- A note name followed by **maj7** means a major triad with a major 7th from the root:
  G^{maj7} = G with a major 7th (G B D F♯)   **E^{maj7}** = E with a major 7th (E G♯ B D♯)

- A note name followed by **dim^7** means a diminished 7th chord:
  Edim^7 = E diminished 7th (E G B♭ D♭)   **Bdim^7** = B diminished 7th (B D F A♭)

- A note name followed by **m$^{7♭5}$** or **m$^{7♮5}$** means a half-diminished 7th chord (i.e. a diminished triad plus a *minor* 7th):
  Em$^{7♭5}$ = E half-diminished 7th (E G B♭ D)
  Bm$^{7♮5}$ = B half-diminished 7th (B D F(♮) A) – note that a natural sign is required in this example because Bm means B D F♯, whereas we need B D F♮ A.

You may come across some of these chords labelled slightly differently from what is shown here. For example, minor chords are sometimes indicated by the abbreviation 'min' rather than just 'm', and other symbols may be used, such as ° for a diminished chord, ∅ to indicate a half-diminished 7th, or △ for a major 7th chord. You may also see the abbreviation 'sus' for a chord that includes a suspension – we look at this in more detail on page 110.

In exams you can use any recognised system for indicating the specific types of chord you choose, provided that you do so consistently.

Some important general points about chord symbols:

✦ Chord symbols do *not* take account of the key signature (if there is one). So, if there is a B♭ in the key signature, the chord symbol **G** does *not* mean G B♭ D – it means G B♮ D. You must write **Gm** if you want G B♭ D, even when B♭ is present in the key signature.

✦ The numeral ^{7} after a letter name, and with no other symbol, always indicates a *minor* 7th above the letter name. So $\mathbf{C}^7$ always means C E G B♭, not C E G B♮, even if there is no B♭ in the key signature.

✦ Most chord symbols have a single letter, with or without an accidental, which tells you the root of the chord. The chord symbol as a whole represents the chord in root position. So **F** means the notes F A C with an F sounding in the bass, while $\mathbf{F\sharp m}^7$ means the notes F♯ A C♯ E, with an F♯ sounding in the bass.

Slash chords

When you want a chord whose root does not come in the bass, you have to write a forward slash after the chord symbol followed by the name of the actual bass note. For example, C/E means a chord of C major (C E G) with E in the bass. This type of symbol is known as a **slash chord** (or **slashed chord**).

Many slash chords indicate inversions. Here are some examples:

✦ **G/B** = a chord of G, with B in the bass (B D G – a first-inversion chord)

✦ **Cm/G** = a chord of C minor, with G in the bass (G C E♭ – a second inversion)

✦ $\mathbf{Gm}^7\mathbf{/F}$ = a G minor 7th chord, with F in the bass (F G B♭ D – a third inversion)

✦ $\mathbf{F\sharp dim}^7\mathbf{/A}$ = a diminished 7th on F♯, with A in the bass (A C E♭ F♯).

Slash chords are also used if there is a pedal in the bass above which the chords change, for example: **C   F/C   G/C   C.**

They are also needed if the chord remains the same but the bass moves on important beats. The following symbols indicate a repeated chord of E minor below which the bass descends chromatically: **Em   Em/D♯   Em/D   Em/C♯   Em/C   Em/B.**

Activity 4.2

For each symbol below, describe the kind of chord required and give the letter names of all its notes. For example, $\mathbf{D}^7$ is a 7th chord on D (D F♯ A C). Play each chord.

F	Fm	Fdim	F/A	$\mathbf{F}^7$	$\mathbf{Fm}^7$	$\mathbf{F}^{maj7}$
E	E♭	Bm	C♯m	Adim	F♯dim	D/F♯
Dm/F	B♭/F	$\mathbf{B}^7$	$\mathbf{A\flat}^7$	$\mathbf{Am}^7$	$\mathbf{B\flat m}^7$	$\mathbf{C}^{maj7}$

4.3 Melody and bass ranges

Ex. 4.3
Voice

Bass guitar

The top part in the exercises that follow, like those in the Edexcel exam, are written in the treble clef and are intended for singing, even though no words are provided. In sections where you have to add a melody, be guided by the range of the given material, although it's often good to go a little beyond that, especially in the upward direction. An overall vocal range of as much as a 12th may be possible if the given material suggests a part with a wide range (see *left*). Notes up to G (or even A) may be appropriate for moments of melodic climax, but for most of the time it is best not to use notes on leger lines, apart from middle C.

Bass parts are for four-string bass guitar and should not exceed the range shown *left* – be careful not to write any note lower than E just below the bass stave. Note that the bass guitar sounds an octave lower than written.

4.4 Choosing melody notes for each chord symbol

To be able to add a melody to a given bass, we must know how to choose suitable notes for each chord symbol. For any chord symbol there may be times, particularly at the end of a phrase, when just one melody note is needed. This could be any note from the chord, although in the case of slash chords it's best to avoid doubling the bass note (that is, the note following the slash sign) in the melody. For instance, if the chord is **Em/D♯** avoid using D♯ in the melody and choose E, G or B instead.

In the early stages you may find it helps to write out the names of the notes that make up each chord before selecting the one(s) to use (e.g. B♭, D, F for a B♭ chord).

Activity 4.4.1

In each example *below*, complete the second bar by writing the correct bass note on the lower stave and one appropriate note from the given chord on the upper stave. Choose melody notes that do not require a large leap from the previous note, and remember not to double the bass note of any slash chords.

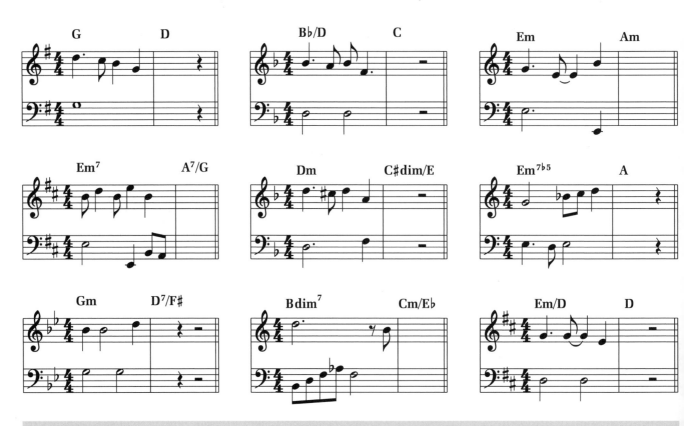

| **Using two or more melody notes for each chord** | Most chord symbols will need more than one melody note in order to produce an effective vocal line. There are three possibilities, all of which can be combined: |

1. You can repeat a single pitch, although this shouldn't be overdone. Try to repeat, or develop, rhythms from the given parts of the melody or rhythms that you have used earlier in the exercise.

2. You can use two or more different notes from the given chord, providing that the melodic intervals between them are singable and that they fit in well with the surrounding notes.

3. You can add non-chord notes in order to create a more interesting or less jagged melodic contour.

Here are some simple examples of methods 1 and 2, based on a chord of A. Two notes of equal value are used in (a) and two notes of different value in (b). In example (c) both pitches have been repeated. In an actual exercise, the rhythms you choose will depend on how the bar concerned fits in with the overall shape of the melody.

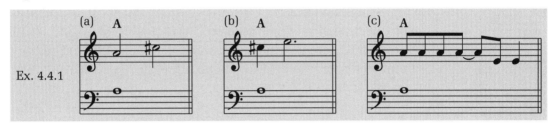

Ex. 4.4.1

You can, of course, use more than two pitches from the given chord. For example, a melody to a chord of G minor might include G, B♭ and D (not necessarily in that order), with or without repeating any of the notes:

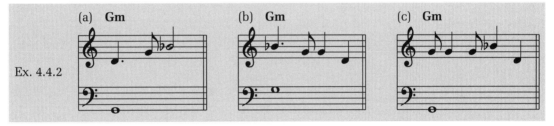

Ex. 4.4.2

Activity 4.4.2

Turn to Activity 4.2 on page 95. Using two staves, treble and bass, write the appropriate bass note as a semibreve and then add a bar of melody notes above it, using *two or more* notes for each chord. Don't use a key signature, but indicate any sharps or flats as accidentals, and remember not to include the bass note of slash chords among your melody notes.

| **Using non-chord notes** | We can add even more variety and interest by using non-chord notes such as passing notes, auxiliaries, appoggiaturas and anticipations (revise Chapter 4 of the *AS Music Harmony Workbook* if you are unsure of these terms). |

Composers of popular music are generally much freer in their handling of part-writing and dissonance than 18th-century composers such as Bach. They tend to think of such notes as a way of providing additional interest and variety rather than in terms of strict part-writing rules. Nevertheless, non-chord notes are usually approached and quitted logically in popular songs – composers don't use random pitches that make no musical sense. In particular, you won't often find leaps to and from non-chord notes that fall *totally* outside the classical rules that you encountered in *AS Music Harmony Workbook*.

Look at the following examples, and try to identify what happens in each before reading the commentary *below*.

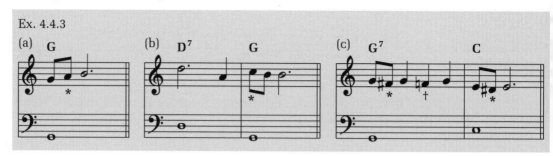

Ex. 4.4.3

In (a), the note marked ✱ is a passing note between two harmony notes, G and B.

In (b) the note marked ✱ is an appoggiatura, resolving to B.

In (c), both notes marked ✱ are chromatic lower auxiliaries that occur between chord notes on either side. The F♮ (marked †) is the 7th of G⁷ and is therefore a chord note. Notice that it is approached by step and that it resolves to E, although not immediately – the melody returns to G before falling to E. Such delayed resolutions are common in many different styles of music.

Now let's look at three more examples:

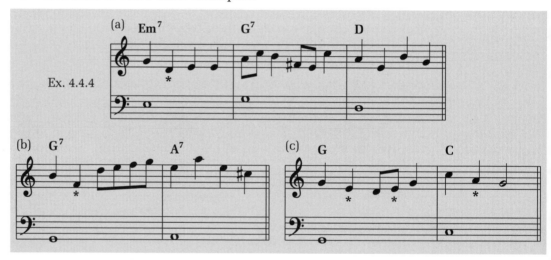

Ex. 4.4.4

In (a), the note marked ✱ is the 7th of Em⁷ and would have been out of order in Bach's day because it is neither prepared nor resolved. Such totally free treatment of a 7th sometimes occurs in popular ballads, but the passage as a whole is not good. The A at the start of bar 2 clashes against G in the bass and, instead of resolving, it leaps to another dissonance (C), while the F♯ clashes with the F♮ that is a vital part of the **G⁷** chord in this bar. In bar 3 the A on the first beat is followed by leaps between non-chord notes which make no musical sense.

In (b), the note marked ✱ is the 7th of G⁷ and so is a correct chord note, but it sounds very isolated – there's no neighbouring note that's close in pitch to it. The high F later in the bar works much better – it is approached and quitted by step and it resolves to E in bar 2 (after an intervening quaver G). In popular-song exercises:

✦ Prepare 7ths, or approach them by step or by a leap from another chord note

✦ Resolve 7ths (making them fall by step) when the chord changes, even if you decide to use an intervening chord note before the resolution.

In (c), the notes marked ✱ are a type of melodic decoration that is very common in popular music from the 19th century onwards. They are all a major 6th above the

An added 6th can also be specified in a chord symbol. For example, C^6 means a triad of C major plus the note A.

root of their respective chords. Such **added 6ths** can be treated a little more freely than most other non-chord notes and don't always move by step. For instance, the first E in Example 4.4.4 (c) is approached by a leap from a chord note, as is the A in bar 2, while the second E is quitted by leap to a chord note.

To sum up: dissonances in popular-song exercises generally resolve by step, usually downwards. Avoid leaping randomly from or to a non-chord note. If in doubt, follow classical ways of treating non-chord notes.

Activity 4.4.3

(a) (i) Add a single note at * to resolve the 7th of chord G^7 in example (i).
   (ii) Add three passing notes to the melody in example (ii).
   (iii) In example (iii) add a diatonic lower auxiliary note to the melody in bar 1 and a chromatic lower auxiliary note to the melody in bar 2.

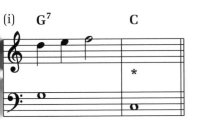

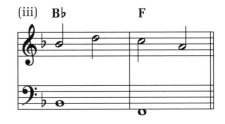

(b) Complete each of the following passages by adding a melody to fit the given bass and chord symbols. Include suitably approached and quitted non-chord notes in each melody.

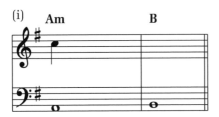

4.5 Building a melody

To add a full melody part above a given bass with chord symbols:

1 Identify the key(s)

Decide what the key is at the start and check for any change(s) of key. A full method for identifying keys is given in the *AS Music Harmony Workbook*, page 70. Being aware of the key signature and the key(s) of music is vital to fully understanding the given material, in particular where the chord progressions are leading and what accidentals are needed. Just working out the chord symbols one at a time is not enough.

2 Add a single note for each chord symbol or on each minim beat

Write one note in the vocal part where each new chord symbol begins, to provide an outline from which you can later build a complete melody. Use noteheads rather than precise note values to show that this is still just an outline. Where a single chord symbol serves for a whole bar, you may want to write in a notehead for each minim beat, except, for example, on the concluding tonic chord of a piece.

Remember that for each chord or minim beat, you can choose any of the notes allowed by the current chord symbol, provided that it fits well into the passage as a whole. This means, for example, that in bar 4 *below* you don't have to include the 7th of the D^7 chord in your melody – you're free to choose any other note of this chord.

Watch for consecutive octaves and consecutive 5ths between melody and bass, even in your outline. Consecutive octaves are best avoided altogether, because they tend to rob the two parts of their independence. There is no ban on consecutive 5ths as in chorales and in Baroque counterpoint, but avoid them unless you're really sure that they work (which they may do in the deliberate parallel chord-progressions that are common in some popular music).

3   Complete the melody

Add additional harmony notes and non-chord notes to your outline. Aim to create a convincing rhythm as well as a good melodic outline. (See the guidance on melody writing in the *AS Music Harmony Workbook*, **Section 5.3**, pages 64–65.) Think about the phrase structure. Many popular ballads have two- and four-bar phrases within longer (eight- and 16-bar) structural units. You should take account of this in your melody, perhaps by separating phrases with a rest in which a singer could breathe, since the melody is intended to be a vocal part.

In elaborating your Step 2 outline, you may unintentionally introduce consecutive octaves (if so, remove them) or consecutive 5ths (if so, again remove them, unless they fit really well in the passage concerned).

Make sure that your added part goes well rhythmically with the given bass. The two parts will rarely move along together in the same rhythm, but each will have some independence. It's particularly good for the melody to be less active where the bass is busy, and to have more notes where the bass is slower moving.

4   Check your work

Make sure that your melody agrees with the given chord structure and that all bars have the correct number of beats. Is what you've written successful *as a melody*? Check that your part has some clear relationship to the given material, a sensible range, and a good balance between stepwise movement and leaps. The phrases should be well shaped, with a clear sense of ascending and descending movement. Check that there are no consecutive octaves, and no unwanted parallel 5ths.

We'll now apply this four-step method to the following exercise.

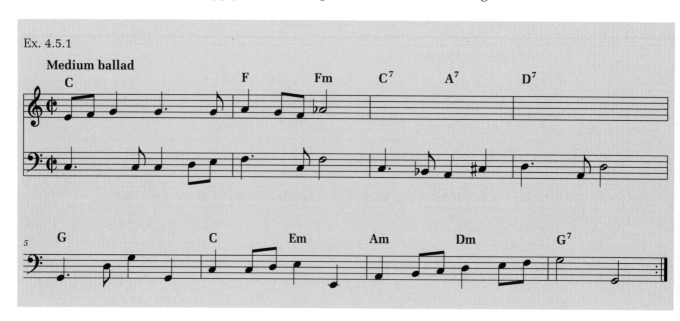

Ex. 4.5.1

We've sometimes referred to chords by using Roman numerals in the discussion that follows. Although they are not widely used in popular music, Roman numerals can sometimes be more useful than chord symbols when planning the harmony for an exercise, because they describe chords in terms of their function, rather than just labelling them in isolation.

Step 1   The exercise starts and ends in C major: G^7 in bar 8 is chord V^7 in C, and leads back to chord I in bar 1 on the repeat. From bar 6, second minim beat, to the return of the opening chord of C, there is a segment from the circle of 5ths.

The music doesn't change key. The Fm chord in bar 2 is a chromatic (flattened) version of chord IV (F A♭ C) following a normal chord IV (F A C) in the first half of the bar. It gives a type of major-minor shift often heard in popular music.

See pages 47–48 of the *AS Music Harmony Workbook* for more on secondary dominants.

The chords from A^7 in bar 3 to C in bar 6 give us another segment from the circle of 5ths, the first two (A^7 and D^7) being chromatic chords (**secondary dominants**). There are no chromatic alterations in the second circle-of-5ths progression which begins in the second half of bar 6.

Step 2   Here is our outline melody, with a notehead at each chord change and at each new minim beat where a chord lasts for a whole bar:

Ex. 4.5.2

Although fairly basic, our outline is more than just a succession of notes to fit the chords: there is already some sense of shape. It covers a reasonable range of notes, but without jumping about randomly. Note also the following details:

✦ G has been chosen for the start of bar 3 not only because it follows on well from the preceding A♭ but also because it prepares the 7th of A^7 (i.e. the note G) in the second half of the bar. This 7th then resolves by falling a semitone to F♯ at the start of bar 4. Although traditional dissonance treatment is not essential in these exercises, the type of ballad style used for the Edexcel technical study is rather closer to classical principles than you would find in rock-based styles.

✦ The melodic climax (the highest note, E) is roughly two-thirds of the way through: not too soon, yet early enough to allow some sense of relaxation before the end.

✦ Bars 6–7 are more angular than the rest, but the intervals are not awkward, thanks partly to careful use of contrary motion.

✦ We've ended on a low F in bar 8 (the 7th of the G^7 chord), to create a smooth transition for the repeat – the 7th will fall by step to E when bar 1 returns.

Step 3 Where the outline has a leap between two noteheads, you can often fill the gap with stepwise movement. For example, the C and A in bar 7 can be linked by a passing note on B. Similarly, the 4th from E to B in bar 6 can be filled in with a passing note on D and a harmony note on C.

If your outline includes adjacent notes that are the same, or just a step apart, you can create rhythmic interest by repeating notes or adding other types of non-chord note such as auxiliaries, appoggiaturas or anticipations.

In order to explore the possibilities, we have produced two different workings. The first includes rests to provide breathing points in the vocal line and some passing notes, but it is a little basic, and bar 5 in particular lacks interest:

Ex. 4.5.3

The next working shows more enterprise – it departs further from the Step 2 outline but this is good if the final outcome is better. There is more melodic decoration, including some accented passing notes (marked *), an appoggiatura (marked †) and a lower auxiliary note (AUX) in bar 6. Rests at the end of each four-bar phrase provide breathing points in the vocal line.

Try to build on melodic ideas in the given material. Here we have used the opening three-note motif (E F G) in bar 5 (transposed up a 5th and then inverted in the second half of the bar) as well as in bar 3 (where it is inverted and then extended):

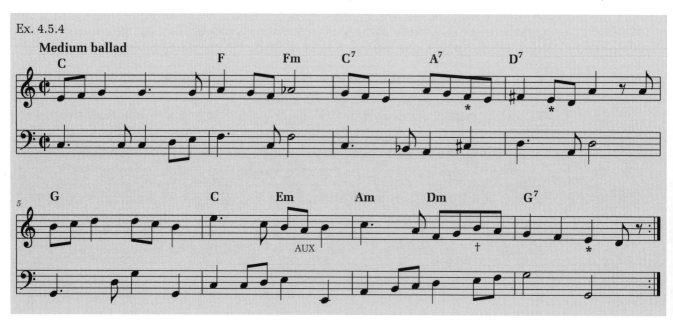

Ex. 4.5.4

Step 4 As always, check your work carefully, ensuring that you have completed every bar with the correct number of beats.

(a) Add one melody note above each bass note in the following passages, taking care to resolve any dissonances. In (ii) the starting note is given and your top part should not include any leaps – just stepwise movement and repeated notes.

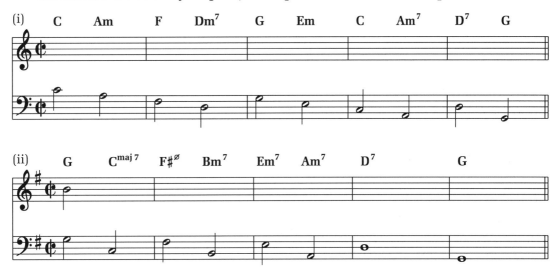

(b) Add a melody to the following bass, using more than one note for each bass note where appropriate. Include some non-chord notes (for example, passing notes). A suggested starting pitch is given. If you wish, try working the exercise again, starting on a different note of the opening chord.

(c) Complete the vocal part in the following passage. The bass is quite busy, so your added part should not be too active – your melodic outline (with a notehead on each minim beat) may not need a great deal of embellishment.

(d) Complete the vocal part of the following passage. It has a less busy bass than (c) so the melody can be more active. The given opening includes syncopations of a kind quite often found in the melodies of popular songs, some of which involve tied anticipations (as for example the E at the end of bar 1).

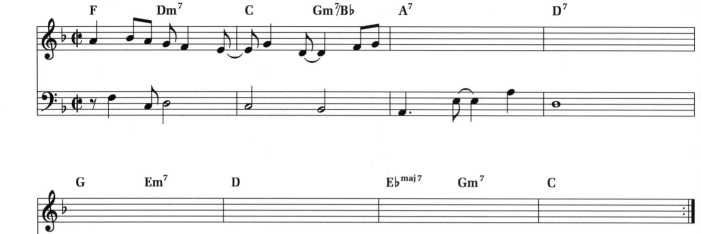

(e) Complete the vocal part in the following passage. The bass is very busy in this example, so the melody can be relatively simple. Remember the general principle that where one part has a lot of notes, it's good for the other part to be less active.

4.6 Adding a bass part and chord symbols to a melody

Writing a good bass part

Because the bass part is instrumental, it can span a wider range of notes than the vocal melody. Aim to use at least the range covered by the given material, and if possible occasionally go higher and/or lower, although keep within the limits for the bass guitar shown in **Section 4.3** (page 96).

Bass parts usually contain more leaps than melodies because they frequently move between roots of chords that are a 4th or a 5th apart. Perfect 4ths in particular are a feature of many popular-style bass parts because the strings of the bass guitar are tuned in 4ths, and so this interval can easily be played on adjacent strings – look, for example, at bars 2 and 4 of Example 4.5.1 on page 100.

Bass parts also include passing notes, auxiliary notes and anticipations to create contrasting stepwise movement. However, on-beat dissonances such as accented passing notes or appoggiaturas are rarely used in the basses of simple ballad styles, as they can obscure the important harmonic function of the bass.

In a good bass part (as in any well-shaped melodic line) ascending and descending patterns are carefully balanced, and there are points of climax and relaxation. Repeated notes can be used, especially within well-defined rhythmic patterns (as shown *below*), but don't over-work such patterns and thereby make your bass too repetitive:

Ex. 4.6.1

Octave leaps can sometimes give more energy to a bass than straight repetition or narrow melodic movement, but they can sound very angular when used frequently. In these ballad-style exercises they should be used only if they suit the character of the rest of the bass part:

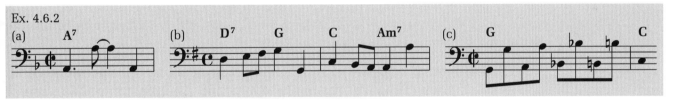

Ex. 4.6.2

Bass parts, like vocal melodies, are strongest when they have **clear phrase structure**. As noted earlier, popular ballads often consist of two-, four- and eight-bar phrases. The ends of phrases may be marked by a long note as in (a) *below,* or by rests as in (b). Using a semibreve for an entire bar *in the middle of a phrase,* as in (c), is less good because the lack of movement makes the bass part too static.

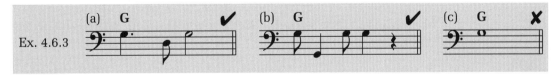

Ex. 4.6.3

An alternative way of treating the last bar of a phrase is to write a **fill** that leads into the next phrase. The bass run in (a) *below* is a simple scale pattern. A more chromatic link is shown in (b), while the fill in (c) starts (rather unusually) on a non-chord note. If you do this, be sure to resolve the dissonance onto a harmony note, as here:

Ex. 4.6.4

If part of the given melody is repeated in sequence, always look to see if the chords will allow the bass to follow the same sequential pattern, as in this example:

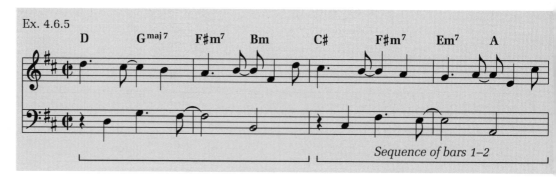

Ex. 4.6.5

Sequence of bars 1–2

Adding a bass and chord symbols

In the sections of the Edexcel test in which you have to add a bass part and chord symbols, start by choosing the chords. *Then* build an outline bass part to match this chordal framework. Finally, add non-chord notes as appropriate to the character of the piece you're working on. Here's the method to use:

1 Identify the key(s) and any cadences

Decide what the key is at the start of the passage concerned, and check for any change(s) of key. Look for possible cadence patterns at the ends of sections and also at the ends of four-bar units within a section. Imperfect cadences, ending on a $V^{(7)}$ (which moves to I at the start of the next phrase) are more common than in most classical styles.

2 Choose and label suitable chords, and write an outline bass part

Look at the parts of the bass and melody that are given to get an idea of the likely **harmonic rhythm** (rate of chord change). Do the chords change once a bar or twice? Do they change more frequently as a cadence approaches? This can only be a rough guide to writing your own chord pattern since, particularly in longer exercises, the harmonic rhythm is unlikely to remain constant.

Next, identify which notes are likely to be harmony notes, and decide which chord will fit best at each change of harmony. You may find it helpful to think in terms of Roman numerals at phrase breaks and cadences. For instance, thinking of a chord at the end of a phrase as V^7 in C major tells you more than G^7 does, because it defines the key and clarifies the chord's dominant function.

Make sure that the chords you choose really do fit the given melody. Notes in the vocal line which are not part of your chosen chord must be melodic decoration, which usually means that they move by step between harmony notes. If you find that you have random jumps to non-harmony notes, you have almost certainly not chosen the best chord for the location.

Your chords must also sound good in succession. In Chapter 3 of the *AS Music Harmony Workbook* we saw that the following progressions usually work well:

✦ Chords with roots a 4th or 5th apart, e.g. F–C or Em–Am–Dm–G–C

✦ Chords whose roots *fall* in 3rds, e.g. C–Am–F–Dm

✦ Chords whose roots *rise* in 2nds e.g. C–Dm. Such parallel progressions, more common in popular music than in classical, should still not be overdone.

Remember that you can sometimes use a 7th chord instead of a triad. Seventh chords often work well if the root of the next chord is a 5th lower (or 4th higher): e.g. Em^7–Am or Dm^7–G^7–C.

Write down the chord symbols as soon as you decide on them. Don't forget to convert any Roman numerals into chord symbols – for instance if you decide to use chord V^7 of C major, your finished score must show it as G^7.

Chord symbols should be placed on the main beat(s) of the bar, even where the melody is syncopated:

Ex. 4.6.6

Before leaving Step 2, write in a bass note (as a notehead) for each chord symbol, to provide an outline for Step 3. Most of these notes will be the roots of chords, so for a chord of D the bass note is D, for Em it is E, for $F\sharp m^7$ it is F$\sharp$, and so on. However, if you have chosen any slash chords, remember that the note *after* the slash is the bass note: for instance, for C/E the bass note is E (see page 95).

3 Complete the bass part

Expand your outline by repeating pitches, adding other notes from the chord plus some non-chord notes, and including occasional short rests.

A good bass part needs rhythmic interest. This doesn't mean making it complicated or fussy – bass rhythms are often repeated several times to different pitches rather than changing in every bar. For example, you could use a rhythm three times (set to different pitches) before employing something simpler (such as a long note followed by a rest) to mark the end of a phrase. Where possible, make use of distinctive rhythm patterns from the given bass part.

Always consider the rhythm of the melody as you work on your bass part. Don't duplicate the vocal rhythm for more than a few notes at a time. In fact, the principle to follow is one we've referred to before. The rhythms of the melody and bass should be contrasting – not in an extreme way, but just so that each part maintains its independence. Use less movement in the bass if the melody is busy and write a more active bass where the melody seems to lack interest. For instance, if the voice has a rest at the end of the phrase, it is more interesting for the bass to fill the gap rather than to duplicate the singer's rest:

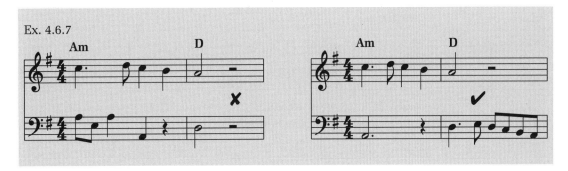

Ex. 4.6.7

Remember that bass parts often have quite a wide range, so be prepared to move notes in your outline to a different octave if it helps create a better contour (but don't go lower than E below the bass stave).

Aim for plenty of contrary motion between melody and bass. In particular, avoid parallel octaves and (unless you're convinced they work), parallel 5ths. Such parallel intervals often arise when you use chords that are a step apart, such as C–B♭–Am–Gm. If you find yourself with unwanted parallels, change some of the chords and/or use slash chords – in either case remember to alter your chord symbols to reflect the changes:

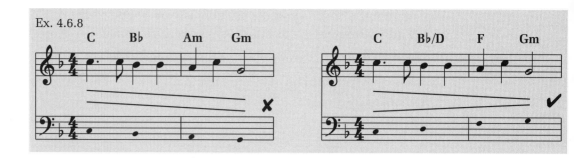

Ex. 4.6.8

4 Check your work

In particular, make sure that any necessary accidentals have been added and that all bars have the correct number of beats.

We'll now complete the following passage, using our four-step method.

Ex. 4.6.9

Medium slow ballad

Step 1   The music begins in C major. Bar 4 is based on G and D, two notes from chord V, implying that the first phrase should end with an imperfect cadence. The two F♯s in bar 5 suggest that the music touches on G major but the single G♯ in bar 6 is best treated as a lower auxiliary note since a move to A minor would be unlikely after so many G♮s in the previous bar.

The Bs and Ds in bar 7, followed by the long C in bar 8, clearly indicate that the second phrase should end with a perfect cadence in the tonic ($G^{(7)}$–C). The third phrase can end with another imperfect perfect cadence, since $G^{(7)}$ will work well in bar 12 and lead back neatly to C when the opening material is repeated.

Step 2   The harmonic rhythm of bars 1–2 is slow: one chord per bar. We can use the same rate of chord change occasionally, but writing two chords in some bars will give greater interest. More than two chords per bar would risk sounding fussy, given the style of the opening.

Step 1 shows that bars 4, 7 and 12 will be based on G or G^7: either is possible, but G^7 gives the harmony a little more richness.

The melody of bar 3 is built mainly on F and A: a chord of F would fit, but we have already decided on G in bar 4, so using F would give parallel octaves between melody and bass. A chord of Dm would therefore be a better choice, especially since we would then have a very effective falling-5ths progression in bars 2–4: Am^7–Dm–G. In our sketch below we have added 7ths to Dm and G, since they follow on well after the Am^7 in bar 2.

Bar 5 calls strongly for Em, given the G–E outline in the melody. Equally, the A–C outline in bar 6 points to Am. But our outline bass part *below* has two chords in each of these bars to give welcome variety to the harmonic rhythm. The progression Am^7–D^7 in bar 6 strengthens the feeling of G major (these two chords are ii^7–V^7 in G major), but there is no actual modulation as the G^7 chord that follows (G, B, D, F♮) bounces us straight back to C major. Notice how the strong falling-5ths progression in this second phrase leads straight into the only perfect cadence of the piece.

How do we deal with the long notes in bars 9–10? Obviously neither is the last chord of a phrase. We could either use two chords in each bar, or we could use one chord per bar but with plenty of movement in the bass to maintain the musical interest. Example 4.6.11 (*overleaf*) shows how this second option might work out.

Chords of C and G would have been possible in bars 9–10, but they have already been used in the two previous bars. We opted for Am and Dm – a strong falling-5ths progression that also offers tonal contrast: they result in the music seeming to head for A minor (Am = chord I, Dm = IV). We have confirmed this as a modulation by using V^7–I of A minor in bar 11 (E^7–Am). But the Am is also chord vi of C major, so it also functions as the first chord of the imperfect cadence in C that concludes the third phrase. The return to C major is confirmed by the G^7 chord in bar 12.

Here is our completed Step 2 outline:

Step 3

The example *overleaf* shows how we filled out this outline to complete the bass part. There are several changes of octave – almost inevitable when you refine a first draft. Study the completed bass and identify as many non-chord notes as you can (e.g. the last quavers of bars 9 and 11 are an anticipation and a passing note respectively).

Ex. 4.6.11

Notice the following points in this working:

✦ Bar 5 has the same rhythm as each of the given bass bars

✦ In bars 9 and 10 we build on this rhythm by adding quavers on beat 4 – an essential development because of the static melody in these bars

✦ Bar 3 introduces a fresh rhythm for variety

✦ Bar 4 is similar to bar 3, but the passing note (F♯) leads pleasantly into the next phrase, and helps point ahead to G major: the false relation that occurs as the F♯ clashes with F♮ in the chord of G^7 (G, B, D, F) is fine since it is very short and in the weakest part of the bar (the final quaver)

✦ The fill in bar 8, which keeps up the momentum during the singer's rest

✦ Patterns in the bass that occasionally anticipate those of the melody: compare the bass in bars 6^2 and 11^1 with the melody in bars 7^1 and 11^2 (melody)

✦ The frequent use of intervals of a 4th in the bass part, reflecting those in the two given bars at the start.

Sus chords

In bar 4 the melody is less active than anywhere else in bars 1–7. Although bar 4 is the end of a phrase, and its simpler rhythm therefore helps articulate the piece, we may still consider that not enough is happening. A possible refinement is to change the chord to G^7**sus** (with G^7 following on the second minim beat).

Ex. 4.6.12

A **sus chord** is a chord in which a 4th replaces the 3rd: G^7sus (or G^7sus4, as it can also be called) is shown *left*. The 4th sounds like a suspension ('sus' is an abbreviation of suspended) but in popular music the suspended note (C in this case) is often not prepared in the previous chord – although here it could be, since C occurs in the Dm^7 chord of bar 3. The suspended note is also not always resolved, although in ballad styles you should normally allow for a resolution. Here, the C could resolve to B when G^7 replaces G^7sus in the second half of the bar.

(i) Rewrite the bass part of bars 9–10 from the example opposite to use two chords in each bar, as shown below.

(ii) Add chord symbols and bass notes to each of the following short passages. For additional practice you could try more than one solution to each. For instance, in the first example you could provide two semibreves as one working, and then something a little more active, or you could try harmonising the two notes with a different pair of chords.

(iii) Complete the bass part and chord symbols in the following passage. Start by identifying the key(s) and aim for a simple working, with just semibreves and minims in the bass. There are only a few non-chord notes in the melody, all on weak beats.

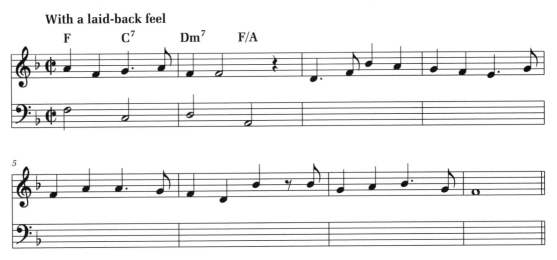

(iv) Produce a more ambitious version of the previous exercise. Bars 1–2 of the bass are given *below*. Include one or two syncopations in your own working, as well as a few other quicker notes.

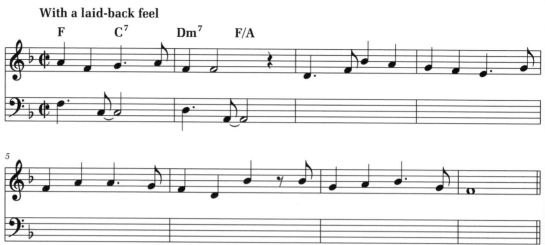

(v) The following is an elaboration of the melody in the last two exercises. Try adapting the bass and, if necessary, the chords you wrote for exercise (iii) or (iv) to suit this version. You will need to recognise where the non-chord notes come – this time some of them sound on strong beats.

(vi) Complete the bass part and chord symbols in the following passage. Both the G♯ at the end of bar 5 and the F at the end of bar 6 are anticipations. Bars 3 and 7 are very similar, but it is best to treat them differently: consider the likely keys in bars 3–4 and 7–8. See the note about rests on the next page.

A notes about rests

Where the vocal part has a rest at the start of a bar or a beat (as in bars 1–3 and 8 of exercise (vi) on the previous page) the harmony begins at the start of the rest and you should write a bass note at this point (as in bars 1, 9 and 13 of the passage *below*).

Where a rest comes later in the bar, the most recent chord continues through the rest. For example, the chord you chose for the start of bar 4 in exercise (vi) will remain in force for the entire bar unless you wrote a new chord symbol later in that bar. (As you probably spotted, the bass needs to keep moving at this point.)

If a melody includes a whole bar's rest at the end of a phrase, or finishes with a note that spans more than a single bar (as in bars 17–18 *below*) it is better to prolong the chord before the rest than to anticipate the first chord of the next phrase.

4.7 Preparatory exercises for Edexcel Unit 5

The exercises in this section combine both skills we have learned in this chapter – writing a melody to fit a given bass and chords, and adding a bass part and chord symbols to a given melody.

(a) Complete the following passage in an appropriate style. Add vocals (without lyrics) to bars 5^2–8b (bar 8b is the last bar in the second system). Add the bass part, with appropriate chord symbols, in bars 11–14 and 16–18.

(b) Complete the following passage in an appropriate style. Add vocals (without lyrics) to bars 4–8 and 19–23. Add a bass part, with appropriate chord symbols, in bars 11–15 and 28–32.

(c) Complete the following passage in an appropriate style. Add vocals (without lyrics) to bars 3–5, 11–12 and 21–24. Add a bass part, with appropriate chord symbols, in bars 7–8, 14–18 and 29–32.

(d) Complete the following passage in an appropriate style. Add vocals (without lyrics) to bars 3–5 and 19–24. Add a bass part, with appropriate chord symbols, in bars 7–8, 11–16 and 27–30.

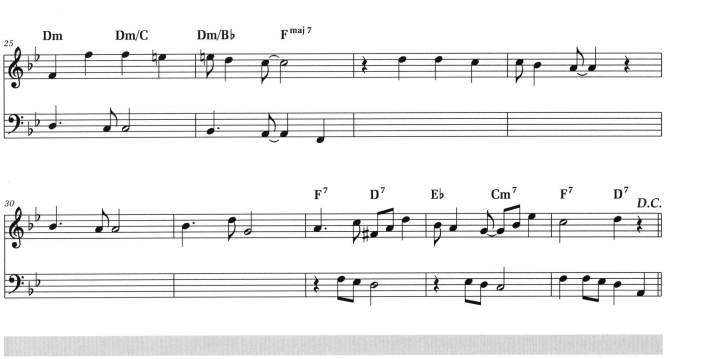

Index